SUMMABLE SERIES AND CONVERGENCE FACTORS

by

CHARLES N. MOORE
Professor of Mathematics, Emeritus,
in the University of Cincinnati

DOVER PUBLICATIONS, INC., NEW YORK

Published in Canada by General Publishing Company, Ltd., 30 Lesmill Road, Don Mills, Toronto, Ontario.

Published in the United Kingdom by Constable and Company, Ltd., 10 Orange Street, London WC 2.

This Dover edition, first published in 1966, is an unabridged and unaltered republication of the work originally published by the American Mathematical Society in 1938 as Volume XXII of the Society's Colloquium Publications. The first edition of this work was published with aid from the Charles Phelps Taft Memorial Fund, University of Cincinnati.

This edition is published by special arrangement with the American Mathematical Society, P. O. Box 6248, Providence, Rhode Island 02904.

Library of Congress Catalog Card Number: 66-23745

Manufactured in the United States of America
Dover Publications, Inc.
180 Varick Street
New York, N. Y. 10014

PREFACE

All methods for summing a divergent series which have come into general use may be classified as mean-value methods or convergence factor methods. Corresponding to any method of either type there can be constructed a formally equivalent method of the other type. The range of validity of the corresponding methods is in general approximately the same. Where there is a difference, it will be in favor of the convergence factor form. A well known instance of this is found in the relative ranges of applicability of Borel's integral definition and Borel's mean-value definition for the sum of a divergent series.

The relationship between a definition based on mean-values and a formally distinct definition in terms of convergence factors was one of the earliest problems studied in the field of divergent series, as is pointed out in the introduction to this book. Subsequently many other results concerning this relationship have been obtained by various workers in the field. Such results are now appropriately termed convergence factor theorems.

One may also be interested primarily in determining the conditions on a set of factors in order that they may preserve convergence for a convergent series or produce convergence for a summable series, when introduced into the terms of such series. The convergence factors used in defining the sum of a divergent series have this property and an additional one as well. To distinguish between the two cases we shall designate as convergence factors of type I those where only the property of maintaining or producing convergence is in question. Factors that may be used to obtain the sum of a series will be known as convergence factors of type II.

The aim of the present work is to give a systematic treatment of convergence factor theorems. Both types of convergence factors are considered, and the theory is developed for multiple series of any order as well as for simply infinite series. Through the use of Nörlund means in place of Cesàro means, the theory developed is considerably more general than that found in the existing literature. Many previous results thus appear as special cases of the theorems proved here, particularly the theorems in the third, fourth, and fifth chapters.

The writer takes pleasure in expressing here his appreciation of encouragement and assistance from various sources in connection with the preparation of this book. He was enabled to spend the entire academic year of 1934–1935 in residence at the Institute for Advanced Study through the aid of grants from the Institute and the Charles Phelps Taft Memorial Fund of the University of Cincinnati. During the period referred to, most of the basic research preliminary to the writing of the book was completed and a considerable portion of the manuscript was prepared. In this connection the excellent facilities for mathematical work available at Princeton and the stimulus of the scientific companionship to be found there were extremely helpful. The preparation of the final draft of the manuscript was considerably facilitated by the careful and competent assistance of Dr. W. C. Mitchell, formerly Laws Fellow in Mathematics at the University of Cincinnati.   Further help from the Taft Fund has been available to bear part of the expense for this work and part of the cost of publication.   For all this assistance and for the coöperation of the American Mathematical Society in accepting this book for publication in the Colloquium Series the writer is deeply grateful.

CHARLES N. MOORE

THE UNIVERSITY OF CINCINNATI, 1937

TABLE OF CONTENTS

SUMMABLE SERIES AND CONVERGENCE FACTORS

INTRODUCTION

0.1. Origin of the theory of summable series. The germ of the modern theory of summable series may be found in a remarkable letter written by Leibniz to Christian Wolf, and published in the Acta Eruditorum in 1713 [100].[1] In this letter he deals specifically with the series

$$(1) \qquad\qquad 1 - 1 + 1 - 1 + \cdots ,$$

and discusses first the reasoning by which Guido Grandi sought to justify the value $\frac{1}{2}$ for this series. While feeling that Grandi's arguments left something to be desired, Leibniz, nevertheless, agreed that the value $\frac{1}{2}$ was reasonable on the basis of his "law of continuity" (lex continuitatis), formulated and used in some of his previous writings.[2] This conclusion he arrived at by consideration of the equation

$$(2) \qquad\qquad \frac{1}{1+x} = 1 - x + x^2 - x^3 + \cdots$$

which subsists for values of x numerically less than unity.

Leibniz also felt, however, that there should be some method of obtaining the value $\frac{1}{2}$ directly from the series (1), without the intervention of the series on the right hand side of (2). He therefore proceeded to formulate what he considered a noteworthy solution of the apparent paradox presented by the equation

$$\tfrac{1}{2} = 1 - 1 + 1 - 1 + \cdots .$$

This solution may be paraphrased in the following fashion. If we take the sum of an even number of terms of the series (1), the value is always zero; if we take the sum of an odd number of terms, the value is always unity. When we pass to the case of an infinite number of terms there is no reason to consider that we have either an odd or an even number of terms, and therefore no reason for assigning either the value unity or zero to the series, but rather for assigning some intermediate value. Moreover, in the process of allowing the number of terms to become infinite, the values 1 and 0 for the sums occur with equal frequency. It is therefore justifiable, on the basis of probability, to assign to the infinite series a value intermediate between 1 and 0 which is precisely their arithmetic mean, namely $\frac{1}{2}$.

Leibniz was well aware that his argument here departed considerably from ordinary mathematical procedure. He admits in the following paragraph that

---

[1] Numbers in square brackets are references to the bibliography. Cf. also Leibnizens Mathematische Schriften, edited by C. I. Gerhardt, Part 2, vol. I, Halle, 1858, pp. 382–387.

[2] Cf. the early mathematical manuscripts of Leibniz, translated from Latin texts published by C. I. Gerhardt with critical and historical notes by J. M. Child, Chicago and London, Open Court Co., 1920, pp. 144–158, particularly p. 147. Cf. also [99].

his method of reasoning seems more metaphysical than mathematical.   But he still contends that the procedure is sound, and he goes on to state that there is more use of what he terms "the canon of metaphysical truth (which proceeds beyond the nomenclature of words)," in mathematics, in analysis, and in geometry, than is generally thought.   His line of thought here is evidently akin to the modern procedure of using heuristic methods to arrive at mathematical conclusions, which are then justified by more precise reasoning.   Leibniz would hardly have been so convinced of the validity of his scheme if the value he obtained had not borne the desired relation to equation (2).

That Leibniz's sound mathematical intuitions were adequate to keep him from straining his interpretation of the series (1) too far in dealing with other divergent series may be seen by examining some of his further correspondence with Wolf.[3]   The latter was so pleased with Leibniz's idea that he wished to evaluate the expansion of $1/(1 + x)$ for other values of x for which it diverges. In particular he wished to conclude that

$$\tfrac{1}{3} = 1 - 2 + 4 - \ \ 8 + 16 - \cdots,$$

$$\tfrac{1}{4} = 1 - 3 + 9 - 27 + 81 - \cdots,$$

and so on, by means of some modification of Leibniz's use of the arithmetic mean.   He outlined to Leibniz his procedure, which was as follows.   If we represent by m a certain positive term in the first of the above series, the sum of all positive terms up to and including that term will be $[(m - 1)/3] + m$.   If we represent the numerical value of a certain negative term by m, the sum of the numerical values of all negative terms up to and including that term will be $[(m - 2)/3] + m$.   Since the difference between these expressions is the desired value of the series, 1/3, Wolf was inclined to make the assumption that if in a finite series formed from the above a last negative term was represented in numerical value by m, a last positive term by n, he would be justified in supposing that in passing to infinity he could take $m = n$.   He then proceeded to express the sum of a finite number of terms ending in a positive term as a function of the numerical value of the last negative term, thus getting the value $\tfrac{1}{3}(4m + 1)$. He further expressed the value of the sum of a finite number of terms ending in a negative term as a function of the last positive term, thus obtaining the value $\tfrac{1}{3}(-4n + 1)$.   The arithmetic mean of these two values being $\tfrac{1}{3}(2m - 2n + 1)$, the assumption that he could take $m = n$ at infinity would yield the value 1/3 for the series.

Leibniz, in reply, expressed his interest in Wolf's idea, but questioned the validity of his reasoning.   He called his attention to the fact that in summing series one usually dealt with series whose terms were decreasing, and that even the series (1) could be regarded as the limit of a series with decreasing terms.

[3] Cf. *Briefwechsel zwischen Leibniz und Christian Wolf*, Handschriften der Koeniglichen Bibliothek zu Hannover, edited by C. I. Gerhardt, Halle, 1860.   Letters LXX, LXXI, pp. 143–148.

He particularly objected to the assumption that at infinity $m = n$, when for all finite cases one had the relationship $n = 2m$. Leibniz urged Wolf to consider the matter further in order that the latter might produce something worthy of science and himself.

0.2. **Formal procedure, as developed by Euler.** Euler was undoubtedly considerably influenced in his attitude toward divergent series by the remarks contained in Leibniz's letter. In fact, in one of his interesting memoirs on series [35], he refers explicitly to the letter and reproduces substantially the argument of Leibniz paraphrased above (cf. *Opera Omnia*, p. 589). He made no attempt to generalize Leibniz's procedure with regard to mean values, however, his own genius and the spirit of the times leading him rather toward a use of divergent series in formal operations. In the memoir referred to above (cf. *Opera Omnia*, p. 587) and in other writings he explains clearly his own doctrine as follows: "Whenever an infinite series is obtained as the development of some closed expression, it may be used in mathematical operations as the equivalent of that expression, even for values of the variable for which the series diverges."[4]

Euler's procedure is obviously related to Leibniz's application to series of his law of continuity. In a later paper [36][5] Euler obtains a sum for various divergent trigonometric series by the process of using the binomial expansions of $(1 + x)$ raised to various powers, substituting $(\cos \varphi + i \sin \varphi)$ and $(\cos \varphi - i \sin \varphi)$ for x, and adding and subtracting the results. This procedure is obviously equivalent to evaluating a power series $\sum a_n z^n$, divergent at a point z_0 on its circle of convergence, by taking the limit

$$\lim_{z \to z_0} [a_0 + a_1 z + a_2 z^2 + \cdots].$$

0.3. **Extension of Leibniz's ideas by Daniel Bernoulli.** It was Euler's contemporary and friend, Daniel Bernoulli, who introduced the first extension of Leibniz's mean-value process. In a memoir of 1771 [12] he discusses recurrent series of a general type, proceeding from the very simple case exemplified by the series (1). He designates as "the period" of such a series the set of terms which recur and whose sum is zero; thus the period of the series (1) is $1 - 1$. If there are n terms in the period and the sum of the first k of them is represented by s_{k-1}, he adopts as the sum of the series the expression

$$(3) \qquad \frac{s_0 + s_1 + \cdots + s_{n-1}}{n},$$

and notes, in certain cases, the agreement of this value with

$$(4) \qquad \lim_{x \to 1-0} [u_0 + u_1 x + u_2 x^2 + \cdots].$$

---

[4] Cum autem in Analysi series ex evolutione fractionum seu quanitatum irrationalium vel etiam transcendentium oriantur, in calculo vicissim licebit loco cuiusque seriei eam quantitatem, ex cuius evolutione nascitur, substituere.

[5] Cf. also [37].

He also applies his method to simple trigonometric series such as $\sum \cos nx$, $\sum \sin nx$, which for values of the variable commensurable with π yield recurrent series.

0.4. The convergence factor theorems of Lagrange, Raabe, and Frobenius. A proof that the limit (4) always exists and yields the value (3) for recurrent series of the type considered by Bernoulli was given by Lagrange (cf. [97]) in 1799 in the course of a report on a manuscript by Callet. Later Raabe (cf. [132]) considered the same point, giving a somewhat less simple proof of this result. These two papers may properly be regarded as the beginning of a rigorous treatment of summable divergent series. They furnish the first example of what may be called appropriately a convergence factor theorem. The notion of a convergence factor theorem exists in germ in the writings of Leibniz and Daniel Bernoulli, referred to above. These pioneers, however, restricted their remarks in this connection to special examples and proved no general theorem.

In the year 1880 Frobenius [48] published a very considerable extension of the theorem of Lagrange and Raabe. Instead of considering merely series of recurrent type, where the expression (3) repeats the same value at regular intervals, he made the rather natural generalization of considering series where the same expression tends to a definite limit as n becomes infinite. For this class of series he proved that the limit (4) always exists and has the same value as the limit of (3). The title of Frobenius' paper, *Über die Leibnitzche Reihe*, and his reference to Raabe's article and Leibniz's letter show how directly his theorem traces back to the ideas of Leibniz.

0.5. Further developments in convergence factor theorems. Shortly after the appearance of Frobenius' article Hölder [77] published a generalization of the former's result. In this paper he introduced the method of summation by successive means now known as summability (H) and showed that a series summable (H, k) for any positive integer k, could be summed by the convergence factors $1, x, x^2, \cdots$ to the same value. The next step in the development of summable series is found in Cesàro's well known paper [30] on the multiplication of series, where he introduced the method of summation by weighted means, now known as summability (C). At first glance this paper seems to have no connection with the notion of convergence factors. However, if we introduce the convergence factors $1, x, x^2, \cdots$ into the terms of two convergent series and their Cauchy product, it is evident that the latter series will be summable by this convergence factor method to the appropriate value. It seems quite likely that this fact, together with the convergence factor theorems of Frobenius and Hölder, may have suggested to Cesàro the possibility of summing the product series by a mean-value method.

It was Cesàro's success in the summation of the Cauchy product of two or more series by the use of mean-value methods which suggested to Borel the possibility of applying analogous methods to the summation of divergent power series, in connection with the problem of analytic extension. (See [19], pp. 51–52; [20],

pp. 87–92.) The necessary modifications in previous methods led to introduction of means of infinite range, that is, means involving all partial sums
instead of only a finite number. For the applications to analytic extension
Borel found it useful to replace his original definition by one involving an integral,
now known as Borel's integral. This latter definition is readily seen to be a
convergence factor definition, and its equivalence to the Borel mean in all cases
to which they both apply constitutes a convergence factor theorem. The method
of summation introduced shortly afterwards by Le Roy [105], which furnishes
analytic extension throughout the Mittag-Leffler star, is a convergence factor
method.

The classical result, embodied in what is known as the theory of Poisson's
integral [130],[6] is essentially a convergence factor method for summing the
Fourier development of an arbitrary function. Since the convergence factors
used were equivalent to those occurring in the theorems of Frobenius and
Hölder, it was to be expected that sooner or later the possibility of summing
Fourier series by mean-value methods should be investigated. Such an investigation was made by Fejér [40][7] shortly after the publication of Borel's researches
in the domain of power series. Fejér's fundamental result concerning the
summation of Fourier series by arithmetic means of the first order, was the
beginning of an extensive series of investigations which at present writing
probably constitute the most fruitful field of application of summation of series
by mean-value methods.

In his paper in the Mathematische Annalen [42] Fejér pointed out that the
theorem connected with Poisson's integral could be obtained as a corollary of
his result by the use of the theorem of Frobenius. He also extended the latter
theorem to a more general type of convergence factor (loc. cit., §2) and applied
this generalization to derive other classical results. Shortly after the appearance
of Fejér's paper further generalizations in the field of convergence factor theorems were obtained independently by G. H. Hardy ([62], [63]) and C. N. Moore
[113]. In the latter paper the term convergence factor was first used in connection with general theorems of this type.

In 1908 Bromwich [22] published a theorem on convergence factors in series
summable by Cesàro means of integral order which included the various results
referred to in the previous paragraph. His theorem lacked only a little of being
definitive, for in 1922 W. A. Hurwitz [79] obtained necessary and sufficient
conditions for convergence factors of this type by means of a slight increase in
generality in one of Bromwich's conditions.[8] An extension of Bromwich's
theorem to series summable by Cesàro means of non-integral order was given by
Chapman [31] in 1911.

0.6. **Convergence factor theorems in double series and multiple series of
higher order.** In 1904 Bromwich and Hardy published a generalization of the

------

[6] Cf. also [146] and [13], §3.

[7] Cf. also [41], [42].

[8] For a statement of Hurwitz's conditions cf. [125].

convergence factor theorem of Frobenius and Hölder to multiple series [25]. In 1912, in connection with the summability $(C1)$ of the double Fourier series and its application to certain problems of mathematical physics, C. N. Moore gave an extension to double series [115][9] of Bromwich's theorem for simply infinite series. In 1922 Bess M. Eversull gave the analogous extension to triple series [38]. In 1927 Moore [121] published necessary and sufficient conditions for convergence factors in multiple series summable (Ck) for any integral value of $k \geq 0$. In 1933 [122] these theorems were extended, for double series, to the case of means of non-integral order.

0.7. **Significance of convergence factor methods and convergence factor theorems.** The brief historical sketch which we have given of the origin and early development of the theory of summable series shows what a preponderant influence convergence factor methods and convergence factor theorems had in this connection. This seems only natural, for a convergence factor method of summing a series extends the definition of a function to the end of an interval (or to the limit point of a set of points) in such a manner as to give the function the value which it approaches. If the set of convergence factors used is of a relatively simple character, it seems highly unlikely that the utilization of such definitions could give rise to any contradiction in the field of analysis. It was doubtless an intuitive conviction of this sort which led the early workers in the field of summable series to justify mean-value methods by virtue of their agreement with convergence factor methods. It thus appears that it is highly desirable to have convergence factor theorems of as definitive a nature as possible for all mean-value methods of importance.

In the mathematical solution of many fundamental physical problems we are naturally led to series whose terms contain factors which are the mathematical representations of the damping factors of the physicist. These same factors may be interpreted as convergence factors for summable series, since they satisfy the conditions of the general theorems referred to above. Thus the use of convergence factor theorems and the theory of summable series frequently serves to extend the domain of applicability of the mathematical solution of physical problems. Examples of this may be found for instance in some of the papers of Fejér and of Moore.[10]

Since most definitions of the sum of a divergent series can be thrown into convergence factor form, it is readily seen that convergence factor theorems may be utilized to obtain results concerning relationships of equivalence and inclusion between such methods of summation. In 1914 an application of this sort was made by Moore [118]. In this paper a slight generalization of Bromwich's theorem was used to show that de la Vallée Poussin's method was more general than summation by any Cesàro mean. Subsequently similar applications of Bromwich's theorem to prove relationships of inclusion between other methods

---

[9] Cf. also [116].
[10] Cf. [42], [114], [116], [119].

of summation and Cesàro's method were made by D. M. Morse [125] and H. L. Garabedian [49].

The developments of functions in infinite series utilized in the various branches of the theory of functions have terms which are formed by attaching a set of constant coefficients to a set of simple functions. Thus, if we know convergence or summability properties of the series formed from the coefficients, we may use convergence factor theorems to determine the domain of convergence of the complete series. In this connection an interesting application of convergence factor theorems for multiple series was made by C. R. Adams [2] in a study of the convergence of multiple factorial series.

0.8. The convergence factor theorems of the present work. Up to the present time most of the convergence factor theorems for summable series which have been developed and applied relate to series summable by Cesàro's method. A considerable extension of this method is found in the so-called Nörlund means [126],[11] where the coefficients of the binomial expansion are replaced by an arbitrary set of constants which may be regarded as the coefficients of a general power series. The main purpose of the present work has been to obtain necessary and sufficient conditions for convergence factors in series summable by Nörlund means of a general type, in the case of simple series, double series, and multiple series of order n. In connection with double and multiple series the discussion has been restricted to series for which the corresponding partial sums form bounded sequences. This is the central problem and the case of greatest interest. The theorems developed in Chapters III, IV, and V for series summable (N) include all the previous results for series summable (C); they furthermore constitute a considerable extension of these results. The proofs are published here for the first time, but the results in the case of simple and double series have been announced in two notes published in the Proceedings of the National Academy of Sciences.[12] Convergence factor theorems for convergent series serve to furnish criteria for the regularity of convergence factor definitions of the sum of a divergent series. They also yield as corollaries theorems concerning sequence transformations that preserve the property of convergence. From the latter theorems we obtain criteria for the regularity of mean-value definitions, such as the Silverman-Toeplitz conditions and their generalizations. In Chapter I of the present work there is carried out from this point of view a systematic discussion of theorems of the general type indicated, both for simple series and sequences and multiple series and sequences. In the case of multiple series and sequences the discussion is restricted, as in the rest of the book, to the situation where the partial sums of the multiple series or the elements of the multiple sequence remain bounded, since results for this case are adequate for the applications to questions of regularity that occur later in the book. Attention should be called, however, to recent work in this general field where the

---

[11] Cf. also [161] and [162].
[12] Cf. [123] and [124].

restriction to bounded sequences has not been made. Various interesting theorems of this nature are due to Adams, Agnew, Hamilton, and Lösch. (Cf. [3], [4], [8], [10], [59], [60], [107], [108], and [109].)

0.9. Restricted convergence and restricted summability of multiple series. In 1912, in connection with a study of the summability $(C1)$ of the double Fourier series corresponding to functions having discontinuities along a curve ([115], [117]) Moore was led to the introduction of the notion of restricted summability of a double series. This differs from summability in the general sense in that the indices of the sequence whose limit is involved, become infinite in such a manner that their ratios remain bounded by two arbitrary positive constants. Restricted convergence may be defined in an analogous manner,[13] and the notion of restricted convergence and restricted summability is readily extensible to multiple series of any order. The extension to triple series was used in 1924 by B. M. Eversull [39] in connection with a study of the summability $(C1)$ of the triple Fourier series. More recently, restricted summability of double and triple series was used by H. L. Miller and Alta Odoms [112] in connection with a study of the summability $(C, r > 0)$ of the double and triple Fourier series.

In 1932 Bochner [14] pointed out the significance of the notion of restricted summability in connection with the behavior of the Poisson summation formula in several variables. In the same year he obtained a theorem concerning the regularity of the arithmetic mean definition for restrictedly convergent multiple series [15a]. More recently he has made an interesting and important application of a related type of restricted summability to the summation of multiple Fourier series [15b]. The method of summability used belongs inherently in the restricted class, since Bochner uses "circular" partial sums in the place of rectangular partial sums. A notable feature of his results is found in the fact that his criteria for summability are of the local type, as contrasted with the situation in the case of rectangular or even square partial sums.

In 1933 Lösch [108] gave a complete discussion of the regularity question considered by Bochner in [15a]. In 1934 he made a comprehensive study of the regularity of factorable transformations of double sequences built up from two triangular matrices, each of which satisfies the Silverman-Toeplitz regularity conditions [109]. Lösch's investigations revealed the fact that such transformations would not in all cases preserve the property of restricted convergence of a double sequence, and in case they did preserve this property, that they would not necessarily yield the same limit for the transformed sequence. He further obtained supplementary conditions on the transformations, which are necessary and sufficient that they do preserve regularity and yield the same limit value, both in the case of bounded sequences and in the more general case where the upper limit of the absolute value of the transformed sequence exists in the restricted sense.

[13] Cf. [117], p. 567, footnote.

In Chapter VI questions of similar nature are studied from the point of view of convergence factors.   Here, as in the rest of the present work, the discussion is confined to the case of double series whose partial sums form bounded sequences.   In that respect, then, the theory is less comprehensive than that given in Lösch's paper.   However, for the type of series considered, the results are more general than those of Lösch.   This appears when they are expressed in terms of sequence transformations, since the transformations are neither required to be factorable nor of finite range.

CHAPTER I

CONVERGENCE FACTORS IN CONVERGENT SERIES[14]

1.1. Convergence factors of type I. Given a series

$$(1) \qquad u_0 + u_1 + u_2 + \cdots + u_n + \cdots$$

and a sequence of functions

$$(2) \qquad f_0(\alpha), f_1(\alpha), \cdots, f_n(\alpha), \cdots$$

defined over a set of points, $E(\alpha)$, in a space of any number of dimensions, with coördinates real or complex. We seek necessary and sufficient conditions on the functions (2) in order that the series

$$(3) \qquad u_0 f_0(\alpha) + u_1 f_1(\alpha) + \cdots + u_n f_n(\alpha) + \cdots$$

may converge in $E(\alpha)$, whenever the series (1) converges.

We set

$$(4) \qquad s_n = \sum_{i=0}^{n} u_i, \qquad \sigma_n(\alpha) = \sum_{i=0}^{n} u_i f_i(\alpha).$$

Then by the well known Abel transformation

$$(5) \qquad \sigma_n(\alpha) = \sum_{i=0}^{n-1} s_i \Delta f_i(\alpha) + s_n f_n(\alpha) \qquad (\Delta f_i = f_i - f_{i+1}).$$

Since the s_i remain bounded for all i, it is apparent that the first term on the right hand side of (5) will tend to a limit as $n \to \infty$, if the series $\sum |\Delta f_i(\alpha)|$ converges. The convergence of this series implies the approach to a limit of $f_n(\alpha)$ as $n \to \infty$, and this is a sufficient condition that the second term tend to a limit as $n \to \infty$. We thus have as a sufficient condition for the convergence of (3) in $E(\alpha)$

$$(A) \qquad \sum_{n=0}^{\infty} |\Delta f_n(\alpha)| < K(\alpha) \qquad\qquad E(\alpha),$$

where $K(\alpha)$ is a positive function of α, defined in $E(\alpha)$.

1.2. Necessity of the condition. If (A) does not hold for a particular value of α, α_1, we can select a set of values of n, p_1, p_2, p_3, $\cdots$ $(p_{r+1} - p_r \geqq 2)$, such that if we define

$$\tau_p = \sum_{n=0}^{p} |\Delta f_n(\alpha_1)|,$$

$$|\tau_{p_{r+1}} - \tau_{p_r+1}| > 1 \qquad\qquad (r = 1, 2, 3, \cdots).$$

[14] To avoid frequent footnotes, references to the literature concerning the theorems of the present chapter have been relegated largely to the historical summary (1.21).

We then define for any complex quantity $re^{\vartheta i}$

(6) $\operatorname{sgn} re^{\vartheta i} = e^{-\vartheta i}$, $\operatorname{sgn} 0 = 1$,

and consider the special series (1) for which

$$s_m = [\operatorname{sgn} \Delta f_m(\alpha_1)] \, n^{-1} \qquad (p_n + 1 < m \leq p_{n+1} \, ; n = 1, 2, \cdots),$$

$$s_m = 0 \qquad (0 \leq m \leq p_1 + 1, m = p_2 + 1, p_3 + 1, \cdots).$$

This series obviously converges to zero, but we see from the identity (5) that the series (3) with the $f_n(\alpha)$ we are considering, diverges for $\alpha = \alpha_1$. Thus the necessity of (A) is established.

We may state our results in the following form:

THEOREM I. *The necessary and sufficient condition that the series (3) converge in $E(\alpha)$ whenever the series (1) converges, is that the functions (2) satisfy condition (A).*

1.3. Sequence to function transformations.

Given any convergent sequence

(7) $s_0, s_1, s_2, \cdots, s_n, \cdots$

and a set of functions

(8) $\varphi_0(\alpha), \varphi_1(\alpha), \cdots, \varphi_n(\alpha), \cdots,$

defined over a set of points $E(\alpha)$, of the same nature as that specified in 1.1, we seek necessary and sufficient conditions that the series

(9) $s_0 \varphi_0(\alpha) + s_1 \varphi_1(\alpha) + \cdots + s_n \varphi_n(\alpha) + \cdots$

converge in $E(\alpha)$. From the special case $s_n = 1$ $(n = 0, 1, 2, \cdots)$, we see that the series whose terms are the functions (8) must converge in $E(\alpha)$, and therefore we may define a set of functions $f_n(\alpha)$ by the equations

(10) $f_n(\alpha) = \varphi_n(\alpha) + \varphi_{n+1}(\alpha) + \cdots$ $(n = 0, 1, 2, \cdots).$

From (10) we readily obtain

(11) $\Delta f_n = \varphi_n(\alpha)$ $(n = 0, 1, 2, \cdots).$

If we define the series (1) in terms of the sequence (7) by means of (4), we may write the identity (5) in the form

(12) $\displaystyle\sum_{i=0}^{n-1} s_i \varphi_i(\alpha) = \sigma_n(\alpha) - s_n f_n(\alpha).$

Since, from (10), the second term on the right hand side of (12) approaches zero as n becomes infinite, it is apparent that the series (9) converges when and only when the series (3) converges. We may therefore obtain a necessary and sufficient condition for the convergence of (9) from that already obtained for the convergence of (3). We see from (11) that condition (A) may be written in the form

$$(A^*) \qquad \sum_{n=0}^{\infty} |\varphi_n(\alpha)| < M(\alpha) \qquad\qquad E(\alpha).$$

We have then the result:

LEMMA 1. *The necessary and sufficient condition that the series* (9) *converge in* $E(\alpha)$, *whenever the sequence* (7) *converges is that the set of functions* (8) *satisfy* (A*). *In this case the value of* (9) *is identical with that of the related series with convergence factors* (3).

1.4. Convergence factors of type II. We consider next the case where the functions (2) are of such a nature that each approaches a definite limit as α approaches a limit point α_0, not in $E(\alpha)$. This limit point may have one or more of its coordinates infinite. If the value approached by each $f_n(\alpha)$ is unity, we would naturally wish the function defined by (3) to approach the value of the series (1) as $\alpha \to \alpha_0$.

We consider first the case where $s_n \to 0$ as $n \to \infty$, and in the identity (5) we allow n to become infinite, thus obtaining

$$(13) \qquad \sum_{n=0}^{\infty} u_n f_n(\alpha) = \sum_{n=0}^{\infty} s_n \Delta f_n(\alpha).$$

We readily see that when the $f_n(\alpha)$ all tend to the same value as $\alpha \to \alpha_0$, the right hand side of (13) will tend to zero as $\alpha \to \alpha_0$, provided the series $\sum |\Delta f_n(\alpha)|$ remains uniformly bounded in a certain neighborhood of α_0. We are therefore led to add to (A) the conditions

$$(A_1) \qquad \sum_{n=0}^{\infty} |\Delta f_n(\alpha)| < K \qquad\qquad E'(\alpha),$$

$$(C) \qquad \lim_{\alpha \to \alpha_0} f_n(\alpha) = 1 \qquad\qquad (\text{all } n),$$

where $E'(\alpha)$ contains all the points of $E(\alpha)$ lying in a certain neighborhood of α_0. Since the case where $s_n \to s \neq 0$ can be readily reduced to the case discussed by subtracting s from the first term of (1), we see that the conditions (A), (A_1), and (C) are sufficient that the series (3) converge in $E(\alpha)$ and approach the value of the series (1) as $\alpha \to \alpha_0$.

1.5. Necessity of the conditions. The necessity of (A) having been established in the proof of Theorem I, we need only consider (A_1) and (C). Let us take up first conditions (C). Choose a series (1) which is convergent to $s \neq 0$, and let $\sum u_r^{(1)}$ be a series for which $u_n^{(1)} = u_n - s$ whereas the other terms are identical with those of (1). We have then

$$\sum_{r=0}^{\infty} u_r^{(1)} f_r(\alpha) + s f_n(\alpha) = \sum_{r=0}^{\infty} u_r f_r(\alpha).$$

When $\alpha \to \alpha_0$ the series on the left hand side tends to zero, whereas the series on the right hand side tends to s.   Hence the second term on the left hand side tends to s, or $f_n(\alpha)$ tends to unity.   Thus the necessity of (C) is established.

Consider next (A$_1$).   If it does not hold for any subset of $E(\alpha)$, having α_0 as a limit point, we can select from $E(\alpha)$ a sequence $\alpha^{(m)}$, approaching α_0, such that

$$\sum_{r=0}^{p} |\Delta f_r(\alpha^{(m)})| > m \qquad (m = 1, 2, 3, \cdots)$$

for a proper choice of p (depending on m).   For any particular value of m, m_1, let α_1 and p_1 be the corresponding values of α and p.   Choose $q_1 > p_1$ and define

$$s_r = \text{sgn} \, (\Delta f_r(\alpha_1)) \, m_1^{-\frac{1}{2}} \qquad (0 \leqq r \leqq q_1).$$

Now choose α_2 from the sequence $\alpha^{(m)}$ such that

$$\sum_{r=0}^{q_1} |\Delta f_r(\alpha_2)| < \tfrac{1}{3},$$

which we can do in view of the necessity of (C) already established, and let $m_2 > m_1$, and p_2 be the corresponding values of m and p for which the first inequality above holds.   Take $q_2 > p_2$ and such that

$$\sum_{r=q_2+1}^{\infty} |\Delta f_r(\alpha_2)| < \tfrac{1}{3},$$

which is possible in view of the necessity of (A) established in the proof of Theorem I.   We now define

$$s_r = \text{sgn} \, (\Delta f_r(\alpha_2)) \, m_2^{-\frac{1}{2}} \qquad (q_1 < r \leqq q_2).$$

Then we have, for any series where the further s_r are chosen such that $|s_r| < 1$,

$$\left| \sum_{r=0}^{\infty} s_r \Delta f_r(\alpha_2) \right| \geqq \left| \sum_{r=q_1+1}^{q_2} s_r \Delta f_r(\alpha_2) \right| - \left| \sum_{r=0}^{q_1} s_r \Delta f_r(\alpha_2) \right| - \left| \sum_{r=q_2+1}^{\infty} s_r \Delta f_r(\alpha_2) \right|$$

$$\geqq \frac{1}{m_2^{\frac{1}{2}}} \sum_{r=0}^{q_2} |\Delta f_r(\alpha_2)| - \frac{1}{m_2^{\frac{1}{2}}} \sum_{r=0}^{q_1} |\Delta f_r(\alpha_2)| - \sum_{r=0}^{q_1} |\Delta f_r(\alpha_2)| - \sum_{r=q_2+1}^{\infty} |\Delta f_r(\alpha_2)|$$

$$> m_2^{\frac{1}{2}} - 1.$$

Continuing in this fashion, we define a series convergent to zero, for which the absolute value of the left hand side of (13) increases indefinitely over a set of values α, having α_0 as a limit point.   Thus we have a contradiction, and the necessity of (A$_1$) is established.

We may summarize our results in the following theorem:

THEOREM II.   *The necessary and sufficient conditions that the series* (3) *converge in* $E(\alpha)$, *whenever the series* (1) *is convergent, and approach the value of the series* (1) *as* $\alpha \to \alpha_0$, *are that the convergence factors* (2) *satisfy conditions* (A), (A$_1$), *and* (C).

It should be noted that this theorem furnishes the necessary and sufficient conditions that a convergence factor definition of the sum of a series, applicable to divergent series, should yield the appropriate value when applied to any convergent series.

1.6. **Applications of sequence to function transformations.** In the theory of summable series we frequently ascribe a value to a divergent series by means of a sequence to function transformation, the sequences being formed from the partial sums of the series. In this case the limit of the expression of the form (9) exists as α approaches a certain limit point α_0, and this limit is used as the value of the series. It is highly important to distinguish the cases where the process, applied to a convergent series, will yield the value to which the series converges. We readily obtain necessary and sufficient conditions for these cases by the use of Theorem II.

We know from Lemma 1 that (A*) is a necessary and sufficient condition that (9) converge in $E(\alpha)$. Allowing n to become infinite in the identity (12), we obtain the identity

$$(14) \qquad \sum_{i=0}^{\infty} s_i \varphi_i(\alpha) = \sum_{i=0}^{\infty} u_i f_i(\alpha),$$

where the $f_n(\alpha)$ are defined by means of (10). Hence the left hand side of (14) approaches a limit as $\alpha \to \alpha_0$, when and only when the right hand side does. Therefore the necessary and sufficient conditions that the left hand side approach s, the limit of s_n as $n \to \infty$, are obtained by expressing the necessary and sufficient conditions of Theorem II in terms of the φ's. We have seen in the proof of Lemma 1 that (A*) is equivalent to (A). In view of (11) (A₁) is equivalent to

$$(A_1^*) \qquad \sum_{n=0}^{\infty} | \varphi_n(\alpha) | < K \qquad\qquad E'(\alpha).$$

Finally from (C) and the use of (11) and (10) we may infer that

$$(C_1) \qquad \lim_{\alpha \to \alpha_0} \varphi_n(\alpha) = 0 \qquad\qquad (\text{all } n),$$

$$(C_2) \qquad \lim_{\alpha \to \alpha_0} [\varphi_0(\alpha) + \varphi_1(\alpha) + \cdots + \varphi_n(\alpha) + \cdots] = 1,$$

and these two conditions together enable us to infer (C). We thus have the result:

THEOREM III. *The necessary and sufficient conditions that the limit of* (9) *as* $\alpha \to \alpha_0$ *shall be* s, *for every sequence* s_n *converging to* s, *are* (A*), (A₁*), (C₁), *and* (C₂).

For any sequence to function transformation that enables us to evaluate every convergent sequence to the appropriate limit, we obtain from equation (10) a set of convergence factors that will evaluate the corresponding convergent series to the proper limit. The converse, however, is not true. For if we start with a set of convergence factors satisfying the conditions of Theorem II and define the $\varphi_n(\alpha)$ for the corresponding sequence to function transformation by means of (11), we have as before the identity (12).   Condition (A) enables us to infer the existence of the limit as $n \to \infty$ of $f_n(\alpha)$.   If we represent this limit by $f(\alpha)$ and allow n to become infinite in (12), we obtain

$$\sum_{i=0}^{\infty} s_i \varphi_i(\alpha) = \sum_{i=0}^{\infty} u_i f_i(\alpha) - sf(\alpha).$$

If now we allow α to approach α_0, the first term on the right hand side by virtue of Theorem II approaches s, the limit of s_n as $n \to \infty$.   Hence the left hand side will approach s as $\alpha \to \alpha_0$ only in the case where $f(\alpha)$ tends to zero as $\alpha \to \alpha_0$.
   The following choices of $f_n(\alpha)$:

$$f_n(\alpha) = \arctan n\alpha + 1, \qquad f_n(\alpha) = \sin \frac{1}{\alpha} \arctan n\alpha + 1,$$

where we choose arctan $n\alpha$ in the interval $(0, \pi/2)$, give us instances where the corresponding sequence to function transformation approaches the wrong limit in the first case, and no limit in the second case as $\alpha \to 0$.
   1.7. Convergence factors of type I for double series.   Given a convergent double series,

(15)
$$
\begin{aligned}
&u_{00} + u_{01} + u_{02} + \cdots \\
&+\, u_{10} + u_{11} + u_{12} + \cdots \\
&+\, u_{20} + u_{21} + u_{22} + \cdots \\
&+\, \cdots\cdots\cdots\cdots\cdots
\end{aligned}
\qquad \sum_{i=0, j=0}^{\infty,\infty} u_{ij},
$$

and a doubly infinite set of functions,

(16)
$$
\begin{aligned}
&f_{00}(\alpha)\, f_{01}(\alpha)\, f_{02}(\alpha)\, \cdots \\
&f_{10}(\alpha)\, f_{11}(\alpha)\, f_{12}(\alpha)\, \cdots \\
&f_{20}(\alpha)\, f_{21}(\alpha)\, f_{22}(\alpha)\, \cdots \\
&\cdots\cdots\cdots\cdots\cdots
\end{aligned}
\qquad f_{ij}(\alpha)\ (i, j = 0, 1, 2, \cdots),
$$

defined over a set of points $E(\alpha)$ of the type previously considered.   We suppose further that the double series (15) satisfies the condition

(17)
$$|s_{mn}| < C \qquad \left(\text{all } m, n;\ s_{mn} = \sum_{i=0, j=0}^{m,n} u_{ij}\right),$$

where C is a positive constant.   We seek then necessary and sufficient conditions on the functions (16) in order that the series

(18)
$$\sum_{i=0, j=0}^{\infty,\infty} u_{ij} f_{ij}(\alpha)$$

may converge and satisfy the condition analogous to (17).

If we set

(19)
$$\Delta_{10}f_{ij} = f_{ij} - f_{i+1,j}, \qquad \Delta_{01}f_{ij} = f_{ij} - f_{i,j+1},$$
$$\Delta_{11}f_{ij} = \Delta_{10}(\Delta_{01}f_{ij}) = \Delta_{01}(\Delta_{10}f_{ij}) = f_{ij} - f_{i,j+1} - f_{i+1,j} + f_{i+1,j+1},$$

we readily obtain from the generalization to double series of the Abel transformation

(20)
$$\sigma_{pq}(\alpha) = \sum_{i=0,j=0}^{p,q} u_{ij}f_{ij}(\alpha) = \sum_{i=0,j=0}^{p-1,q-1} s_{ij}\Delta_{11}f_{ij}(\alpha)$$
$$+ \sum_{i=0}^{p-1} s_{iq}\Delta_{10}f_{iq}(\alpha) + \sum_{j=0}^{q-1} s_{pj}\Delta_{01}f_{pj}(\alpha) + s_{pq}f_{pq}(\alpha).$$

The form of the first term on the right hand side of (20) readily suggests the condition analogous to condition (A) for the case of single series, namely,

(A)$_2$
$$\sum_{i=0,j=0}^{\infty,\infty} |\Delta_{11}f_{ij}(\alpha)| < K(\alpha) \qquad\qquad E(\alpha),$$

$K(\alpha)$ being a positive function of α.

In order to obtain in their simplest form conditions adequate to deal with the second, third, and fourth terms on the right hand side of (20), we find it desirable to make an auxiliary use of condition (A)$_2$. From the relationships between the Δ_{11}, Δ_{10}, and Δ_{01}, indicated in (19), we readily obtain

$$\sum_{i=q}^{s} \Delta_{11}f_{ij} = \Delta_{10}f_{iq} - \Delta_{10}f_{i,s+1},$$

$$\sum_{i=p}^{r} \Delta_{11}f_{ij} = \Delta_{01}f_{pj} - \Delta_{01}f_{r+1,j}.$$

If now we impose the conditions

(D$_1$)
$$\lim_{n \to \infty} \Delta_{10}f_{in}(\alpha) = 0 \qquad\qquad (E(\alpha); \text{ all } i),$$

(D$_2$)
$$\lim_{m \to \infty} \Delta_{01}f_{mj}(\alpha) = 0 \qquad\qquad (E(\alpha); \text{ all } j),$$

we obtain from the previous equations

(21)
$$\Delta_{10}f_{iq} = \sum_{j=q}^{\infty} \Delta_{11}f_{ij} \qquad\qquad (\text{all } i),$$

$$\Delta_{01}f_{pj} = \sum_{i=p}^{\infty} \Delta_{11}f_{ij} \qquad\qquad (\text{all } j).$$

From equations (19) and (21) we readily obtain

$$f_{00} - f_{m0} = \sum_{i=0,j=0}^{m-1,\infty} \Delta_{11}f_{ij},$$

$$f_{00} - f_{0n} = \sum_{i=0}^{\infty} \sum_{j=0}^{n-1} \Delta_{11} f_{ij}, \qquad f_{m0} - f_{mn} = \sum_{i=m}^{\infty} \sum_{j=0}^{n-1} \Delta_{11} f_{ij}.$$

Hence it follows from condition $(A)_2$ that

$$|f_{00}(\alpha) - f_{m0}(\alpha)| < K(\alpha), \qquad |f_{00}(\alpha) - f_{0n}(\alpha)| < K(\alpha),$$
$$|f_{m0}(\alpha) - f_{mn}(\alpha)| < K(\alpha) \qquad \text{(all } m, n\text{)},$$

and from these three inequalities we readily infer that $f_{mn}(\alpha)$ remains bounded for all (m, n). We may therefore conclude that the last term on the right hand side of (20) tends to zero as p and q become infinite, provided $s_{pq} \to 0$.

From relations (21) and (17) and condition $(A)_2$ we see that the second and third terms on the right hand side of (20) tend to zero as p and $q \to \infty$. The first term approaches a definite limit as p and $q \to \infty$, in view of condition $(A)_2$. Hence for a series (15) converging to zero, conditions $(A)_2$, (D_1), and (D_2) are sufficient for the convergence of (18) in $E(\alpha)$. Since any convergent series can be reduced to this case by alteration of the term u_{00}, which will not affect the convergence of (18), the sufficiency of the conditions for this convergence has been proved in general. Also, for a bounded s_{pq}, it is readily apparent that the conditions are sufficient for each term on the right hand side of (20), and therefore the left hand side, to remain bounded for all p, q.

1.8. Necessity of the conditions. We consider first condition $(A)_2$. If $(A)_2$ does not hold for a certain choice of α, α_1, we can select a set of values of p differing by at least 2, $p_1, p_2, \cdots, p_n, \cdots$, such that if we define

$$\tau_p = \sum_{i=0, j=0}^{p, p} |\Delta_{11} f_{ij}(\alpha_1)|,$$

we shall have

$$\tau_{p_{n+1}} - \tau_{p_n+1} > 1 \qquad (n = 1, 2, 3, \cdots).$$

We may then obtain a contradiction from the identity (20) by using the special series for which

$$s_{ij} = [\text{sgn } \Delta_{11} f_{ij}(\alpha_1)] \, n^{-1} \qquad (p_n + 1 < i \leqq p_{n+1}, 0 \leqq j \leqq p_{n+1};$$
$$0 \leqq i \leqq p_n + 1, p_n + 1 < j \leqq p_{n+1}; \quad n = 1, 2, 3, \cdots),$$
$$s_{ij} = 0 \qquad \text{(all other } i, j\text{)}.$$

For this series converges to the value zero and satisfies condition (17). Therefore $\sum u_{ij} f_{ij}(\alpha_1)$ is convergent, or the left hand side of (20) approaches a limit for $\alpha = \alpha_1$, as p and q become infinite. But it is readily seen that with the above choice of s_{ij}, the right hand side of (20) becomes infinite when p and q become infinite by taking on the special set of values $(p_2 + 1, p_2 + 1)$, $(p_3 + 1, p_3 + 1)$, $\cdots$. From this contradiction the necessity of $(A)_2$ follows at once.

Since the proofs of the necessity of (D_1) and (D_2) are analogous, we shall deal only with (D_1). If (D_1) does not hold for a particular α, α_1, and a particular i, i_1, we can find an $\epsilon > 0$ such that

$$|\Delta_{10} f_{i_1 m}(\alpha_1)| > \epsilon$$

for an infinite number of choices of $m, m_1, m_2, \cdots, m_n, \cdots$, each one of which exceeds the previous one by at least 2. We then consider the series for which

$$s_{i_1 m_n} = (-1)^n \left[\operatorname{sgn} \Delta_{10} f_{i_1 m_n}(\alpha_1)\right] \qquad (n = 1, 2, 3, \cdots),$$

$$s_{ij} = 0 \qquad\qquad \text{(all other } i, j\text{)}.$$

This series converges to the value zero and satisfies condition (17). If, in the identity (20), we allow p and q to become infinite in such a manner that q takes on the successive values $m_1, m_2, m_3, \cdots$, while $p > i_1$, the second term on the right hand side will oscillate between values $> \epsilon$ and $< - \epsilon$. The other terms on the right hand side, and the left hand side, will approach definite limits. Thus we shall have a contradiction, and the necessity of (D_1) is established. As pointed out before, the proof of the necessity of (D_2) is entirely analogous.

We have now completely established the following theorem:

THEOREM IV. *The necessary and sufficient conditions that the series* (18) *converge in* $E(\alpha)$, *and that for each* α *its partial sums* $\sigma_{pq}(\alpha)$ *remain bounded for all* (p, q), *whenever the series* (15) *is convergent and satisfies* (17), *are that the functions* (16) *satisfy* $(A)_2$, (D_1), *and* (D_2).

1.9. Sequence to function transformations for double sequences. Given any convergent double sequence

$$(22) \qquad\qquad s_{ij} \qquad\qquad (i, j = 0, 1, 2, \cdots),$$

which satisfies condition (17), and a set of functions

$$(23) \qquad\qquad \varphi_{ij}(\alpha) \qquad\qquad (i, j = 0, 1, 2, \cdots),$$

defined over a set of points $E(\alpha)$ of the type specified in 1.1, we seek necessary and sufficient conditions that the series

$$(24) \qquad\qquad \sum_{i=0, j=0}^{\infty, \infty} s_{ij} \varphi_{ij}(\alpha)$$

should converge in $E(\alpha)$. From the special cases

$$s_{ij} = 1 \qquad (i \geqq p, j \geqq q; p = 0, 1, 2, \cdots, q = 0, 1, 2, \cdots),$$

$$s_{ij} = 0 \qquad\qquad (i < p \text{ or } j < q),$$

we see that we may define a set of functions $f_{pq}(\alpha)$ by the equations

$$(25) \qquad\qquad f_{pq}(\alpha) = \sum_{i=p, j=q}^{\infty, \infty} \varphi_{ij}(\alpha) \qquad (p, q = 0, 1, 2, \cdots),$$

since the series on the right hand side must converge in $E(\alpha)$ if (24) converges for all s_{ij} of the type we are considering. Furthermore from the special cases

$$s_{ij} = 1 \qquad\qquad (i \geqq p, j = q; p, q = 0, 1, 2, \cdots),$$

$$s_{ij} = 0 \qquad\qquad \text{(all other } i, j\text{)},$$

and

$$s_{ij} = 1 \qquad\qquad (i = p, j \geqq q; p, q = 0, 1, 2, \cdots),$$

$$s_{ij} = 0 \qquad\qquad \text{(all other } i, j),$$

we see that the series

(26) $$\sum_{i=p}^{\infty} \varphi_{iq}(\alpha), \qquad \sum_{j=q}^{\infty} \varphi_{pj}(\alpha) \qquad\qquad (p, q = 0, 1, 2, \cdots)$$

are convergent in $E(\alpha)$.

We then obtain from (25) and (26)

(27) $$\Delta_{11} f_{pq}(\alpha) = \varphi_{pq}(\alpha), \qquad \Delta_{10} f_{pq}(\alpha) = \sum_{j=q}^{\infty} \varphi_{pj}(\alpha), \qquad \Delta_{01} f_{pq}(\alpha) = \sum_{i=p}^{\infty} \varphi_{iq}(\alpha).$$

If we define the series (15) in terms of the sequence (22) by means of the equality in (17), we may write the identity (20) in the form

(28) $$\sum_{i=0, j=0}^{p-1, q-1} s_{ij} \varphi_{ij}(\alpha) = \sigma_{pq}(\alpha) - \sum_{i=0}^{p-1} s_{iq} \Delta_{10} f_{iq}(\alpha) - \sum_{j=0}^{q-1} s_{pj} \Delta_{01} f_{pj}(\alpha) - s_{pq} f_{pq}(\alpha).$$

Condition $(A)_2$ of the necessary and sufficient conditions for the convergence of the first term on the right hand side of (28) may, in view of (27), be written in the form

$(A^*)_2$ $$\sum_{i=0, j=0}^{\infty, \infty} | \varphi_{ij}(\alpha) | < K(\alpha) \qquad\qquad E(\alpha).$$

In view of (27) condition $(A^*)_2$ implies the further conditions (D_1) and (D_2) for the functions $f_{pq}(\alpha)$, defined by (25). It is therefore the necessary and sufficient condition for the approach to a limit of the first term on the right hand side of (28). It is obviously a sufficient condition that the left hand side of (28) tend to a limit as p and $q \to \infty$, and it can readily be shown to be necessary. For if $(A^*)_2$ does not hold for a particular α, α_1, and we define

$$\tau_p = \sum_{i=0, j=0}^{p, p} | \varphi_{ij}(\alpha_1) |,$$

we can find a set of values of $p, p_1, p_2, \cdots, p_n, \cdots$, such that

$$\tau_{p_{n+1}} - \tau_{p_n} > 1 \qquad\qquad (n = 1, 2, 3, \cdots).$$

If now we define

$$s_{ij} = [\operatorname{sgn} \varphi_{ij}(\alpha_1)] \, n^{-1}$$

$$(p_n < i \leqq p_{n+1}, 0 \leqq j \leqq p_{n+1}; 0 \leqq i \leqq p_n, p_n < j \leqq p_{n+1}; n = 1, 2, 3, \cdots),$$

we shall have an s_{pq} converging to zero as p and $q \to \infty$, while the left hand side of (28) becomes infinite as p and $q \to \infty$.

In view of (25) and (27), $(A^*)_2$ is sufficient for the approach to zero, as p and

$q \to \infty$, of each of the last three terms on the right hand side of (28). It is therefore sufficient that the left hand side of (28) and the first term on the right hand side tend to the same limit as p and $q \to \infty$. It is also necessary for this purpose, since it is necessary for the convergence of the left hand side.

We have thus the following result:

LEMMA 2. *The necessary and sufficient condition that the series* (24) *converge in* $E(\alpha)$ *for any convergent sequence, satisfying* (17), *is that the functions* (23) *satisfy* (A*)$_2$. *This condition is also necessary and sufficient that the value of* (24) *shall be the same as that of the related series with convergence factors,* (18).

We see that Lemma 2 is related to Theorem IV in much the same manner as Lemma 1 is related to Theorem I.

1.10. **Convergence factors of type II for double series.** We consider next the case where each of the functions (16) approaches a limit as $\alpha \to \alpha_0$, not in $E(\alpha)$. For an s_{pq} tending to zero as $p, q \to \infty$, and a set of convergence factors which satisfy conditions (A)$_2$, (D$_1$), and (D$_2$), we obtain from (20) by allowing p and q to become infinite

$$(29) \qquad \sum_{i=0,j=0}^{\infty,\infty} u_{ij} f_{ij}(\alpha) = \sum_{i=0,j=0}^{\infty,\infty} s_{ij} \Delta_{11} f_{ij}(\alpha).$$

If we add to the conditions on $f_{ij}(\alpha)$ the following further restrictions:

$$(E_1) \qquad \lim_{\alpha \to \alpha_0} \sum_{j=0}^{\infty} |\Delta_{11} f_{ij}(\alpha)| = 0 \qquad (i = 0, 1, 2, \cdots),$$

$$(E_2) \qquad \lim_{\alpha \to \alpha_0} \sum_{i=0}^{\infty} |\Delta_{11} f_{ij}(\alpha)| = 0 \qquad (j = 0, 1, 2, \cdots),$$

$$(C)_2 \qquad \lim_{\alpha \to \alpha_0} f_{ij}(\alpha) = 1 \qquad (i, j = 0, 1, 2, \cdots),$$

we see that the right hand side of (29) will tend to zero as $\alpha \to \alpha_0$, for an s_{pq} satisfying (17) and tending to zero as p and $q \to \infty$, provided $\sum |\Delta_{11} f_{ij}(\alpha)|$ remains uniformly bounded in a certain neighborhood of α_0. We then make the further requirement

$$(A_1)_2 \qquad \sum_{i=0,j=0}^{\infty,\infty} |\Delta_{11} f_{ij}(\alpha)| < K \qquad E'(\alpha),$$

where $E'(\alpha)$ contains all the points of $E(\alpha)$ lying in a certain neighborhood of α_0, and K is a positive constant. Thus we see that conditions (A)$_2$, (A$_1$)$_2$, (D$_1$), (D$_2$), (E$_1$), (E$_2$), and (C)$_2$ are sufficient for the series (18) to converge in $E(\alpha)$ and approach the value of the series (15) as $\alpha \to \alpha_0$, in the case where the s_{pq} for (15) satisfy (17) and tend to zero as $p, q \to \infty$. Since the case where $s_{pq} \to s \neq 0$, can be reduced to the simpler case by alteration of u_{00}, we are assured of the sufficiency of these conditions in this case also.

1.11. **Necessity of the conditions.** The necessity of (A)$_2$, (D$_1$), and (D$_2$) has already been established in 1.8, so we need only consider (A$_1$)$_2$, (E$_1$), (E$_2$), and

(C)$_2$. Consider first condition (C)$_2$. The proof of the necessity of this condition is entirely analogous to the proof of the necessity of (C) of Theorem II, given in 1.5. We turn then to the discussion of (A$_1$)$_2$.

If (A$_1$)$_2$ does not hold for any subset of $E(\alpha)$, having α_0 as a limit point we can select from $E(\alpha)$ a sequence $\alpha^{(m)}$, approaching α_0 , such that

$$(30) \qquad \sum_{i=0,\, j=0}^{p,p} |\,\Delta_{11} f_{ij}(\alpha^{(m)})\,| > m \qquad\qquad (m = 1, 2, 3, \cdots)$$

for a proper choice of p. For any particular value of m, m_1 , let α_1 and p_1 be the corresponding values of α and p. Choose $q_1 > p_1$, and define

$$s_{ij} = \text{sgn } (\Delta_{11} f_{ij}(\alpha_1))\, m_1^{-\frac{1}{2}} \qquad \left(0 \leq {i \atop j} \leq q_1\right).$$

Now choose α_2 from the sequence $\alpha^{(m)}$ such that

$$(31) \qquad \sum_{i=0,\, j=0}^{q_1,q_1} |\,\Delta_{11} f_{ij}(\alpha_2)\,| < \tfrac{1}{3},$$

which we can do in view of the necessity of (C)$_2$ already established, and let $m_2 > m_1$, and p_2 be the corresponding values of m and p for which the inequality (30) holds. Take $q_2 > p_2$ and such that

$$(32) \qquad \sum_{i=0,\, j=0}^{\infty,\infty} |\,\Delta_{11} f_{ij}(\alpha_2)\,| - \sum_{i=0,\, j=0}^{q_2,q_2} |\,\Delta_{11} f_{ij}(\alpha_2)\,| = R_{q_2}(\alpha_2) < \tfrac{1}{3},$$

which is possible in view of the necessity of (A)$_2$. We next define

$$s_{ij} = \text{sgn } (\Delta_{11} f_{ij}(\alpha_2))\, m_2^{-\frac{1}{2}}$$

$$(q_1 < i \leq q_2, 0 \leq j \leq q_2 ; 0 \leq i \leq q_1, q_1 < j \leq q_2).$$

We have then, making use of (31) and (32), for a series where the s_{ij} are all less than unity in absolute value

$$
\begin{aligned}
\left|\sum_{i=0,\, j=0}^{\infty,\infty} s_{ij}\Delta_{11}f_{ij}(\alpha_2)\right| &\geq \left|\sum_{i=0,\, j=q_1+1}^{q_1,q_2} s_{ij}\Delta_{11}f_{ij}(\alpha_2) + \sum_{i=q_1+1,\, j=0}^{q_2,q_2} s_{ij}\Delta_{11}f_{ij}(\alpha_2)\right| \\
(33) \qquad &- \left|\sum_{i=0,\, j=0}^{q_1,q_1} s_{ij}\Delta_{11}f_{ij}(\alpha_2)\right| - \left|\sum_{i=0,\, j=0}^{\infty,\infty} s_{ij}\Delta_{11}f_{ij}(\alpha_2) - \sum_{i=0,\, j=0}^{q_2,q_2} s_{ij}\Delta_{11}f_{ij}(\alpha_2)\right| \\
&\geq \frac{1}{m_2^{\frac{1}{2}}}\sum_{i=0,\, j=0}^{q_2,q_2} |\,\Delta_{11}f_{ij}(\alpha_2)\,| - \frac{1}{m_2^{\frac{1}{2}}}\sum_{i=0,\, j=0}^{q_1,q_1} |\,\Delta_{11}f_{ij}(\alpha_2)\,| - \sum_{i=0,\, j=0}^{q_1,q_1} |\,\Delta_{11}f_{ij}(\alpha_2)\,| \\
&- R_{q_2}(\alpha_2) > m_2^{\frac{1}{2}} - 1.
\end{aligned}
$$

Continuing in this fashion, we define a double series, convergent to zero, for which the absolute value of the left hand side of (29) increases indefinitely over a set of values of α, having α_0 as a limit point. Thus we have a contradiction, and the necessity of (A$_1$)$_2$ is established.

The proofs of the necessity of (E$_1$) and (E$_2$) are entirely analogous, and we will therefore consider only the case of (E₁). If this condition does not hold **we** can find an $\epsilon > 0$ and an m such that

$$\sum_{j=0}^{\infty} | \Delta_{11} f_{mj}(\alpha) |$$

exceeds ϵ for a set of values of α lying in $E(\alpha)$ and having α_0 as a limit point. Choose a value of α, α_1, from this sequence and determine s_1 such that

$$\sum_{j=0}^{s_1} | \Delta_{11} f_{mj}(\alpha_1) | > \tfrac{3}{4}\epsilon, \qquad \sum_{j=s_1+1}^{\infty} | \Delta_{11} f_{mj}(\alpha_1) | < \tfrac{1}{4}\epsilon.$$

Then take

$$s_{mj} = [\operatorname{sgn} \Delta_{11} f_{mj}(\alpha_1)] \qquad\qquad (0 \leqq j \leqq s_1).$$

Next find α_2 such that

$$\sum_{j=0}^{s_1} | \Delta_{11} f_{mj}(\alpha_2) | < \tfrac{1}{8}\epsilon,$$

and choose $s_2 > s_1$ such that

$$\sum_{j=s_1+1}^{s_2} | \Delta_{11} f_{mj}(\alpha_2) | > \tfrac{3}{4}\epsilon, \qquad \sum_{j=s_2+1}^{\infty} | \Delta_{11} f_{mj}(\alpha_2) | < \tfrac{1}{8}\epsilon.$$

Then take

$$s_{mj} = [\operatorname{sgn} \Delta_{11} f_{mj}(\alpha_2)] \qquad\qquad (s_1 < j \leqq s_2).$$

Continue this process for the choice of s_{mj}, and choose all other $s_{ij} = 0$. Thus we shall obtain a series which is convergent to zero, whereas the left hand side of (29) remains $> \tfrac{1}{2}\epsilon$ for an infinite set of values of α, having α_0 as a limit point. This contradiction establishes the necessity of (E₁) and, as stated above, the proof of the necessity of (E₂) is entirely analogous.

We have now established the following theorem:

THEOREM V. *The necessary and sufficient conditions that the series* (18) *converge in $E(\alpha)$ and for each α have its partial sums bounded, whenever the series* (15) *converges and satisfies* (17), *and approach the value of* (15) *when $\alpha \to \alpha_0$, are that the functions* (16) *satisfy* (A)₂, (A₁)₂, (C)₂, (D₁), (D₂), (E₁), *and* (E₂).

We note that this theorem furnishes the necessary and sufficient conditions that a convergence factor definition of the value of a series, applicable to divergent series, should yield the appropriate value when applied to convergent double series which satisfy (17).

1.12. **Application of double sequence to function transformations.** Just as in the case of single sequences, we may make use of a double sequence to function transformation to ascribe a value to a divergent double series, the sequence being formed from the partial sums of the series. We thus seek the limits of an expression of the form (24), this limit to be defined as the value of the double series. Here also it is important to distinguish the cases where this process, applied to a convergent series, will yield the value to which the series converges. For the case of convergent double series whose partial sums remain bounded, we may obtain necessary and sufficient conditions for the property in question by the use of Theorem V.

We know from Lemma 2 that $(A^*)_2$ is the necessary and sufficient condition that (24) converge in $E(\alpha)$, and that under this condition we have the identity

$$(34) \qquad \sum_{i=0,\,j=0}^{\infty,\infty} s_{ij}\,\varphi_{ij}(\alpha) = \sum_{i=0,\,j=0}^{\infty,\infty} u_{ij} f_{ij}(\alpha),$$

$\sum u_{ij}$ being the double series defined by means of the given double sequence, and the $f_{ij}(\alpha)$ the functions defined by (25) and therefore also having the relationships with the $\varphi_{ij}(\alpha)$, given in (27). Hence the necessary and sufficient conditions that the left hand side of (34) approach s, the limit of s_{ij}, may be found by expressing the necessary and sufficient conditions of Theorem V in terms of the $\varphi_{ij}(\alpha)$.

We have seen in the proof of Lemma 2 that $(A^*)_2$ is equivalent to $(A)_2$, (D_1), and (D_2). In view of (27), $(A_1)_2$ is equivalent to

$$(A_1^*)_2 \qquad \sum_{i=0,\,j=0}^{\infty,\infty} |\,\varphi_{ij}(\alpha)\,| < K \qquad\qquad E'(\alpha).$$

In view of (27), (E_1) and (E_2) are entirely equivalent to

$$(E_1^*) \qquad\qquad \lim_{\alpha\to\alpha_0} \sum_{j=0}^{\infty} |\,\varphi_{ij}(\alpha)\,| = 0 \qquad\qquad \text{(all } i\text{)},$$

$$(E_2^*) \qquad\qquad \lim_{\alpha\to\alpha_0} \sum_{i=0}^{\infty} |\,\varphi_{ij}(\alpha)\,| = 0 \qquad\qquad \text{(all } j\text{)}.$$

From $(C)_2$ and (25) we may infer

$$(C^*)_2 \qquad\qquad \lim_{\alpha\to\alpha_0} \sum_{i=0,\,j=0}^{\infty,\infty} \varphi_{ij}(\alpha) = 1,$$

and from this condition and (E_1^*) and (E_2^*) we may by use of (25) and (27) derive $(C)_2$.

We thus have the result embodied in the following theorem:

THEOREM VI. *The necessary and sufficient conditions that the limit of (24) as* $\alpha \to \alpha_0$ *shall be* s, *for every sequence* s_{ij} *satisfying* (17) *and converging to* s, *are that the functions* (23) *satisfy* $(A^*)_2$, $(A_1^*)_2$, $(C^*)_2$, (E_1^*), *and* (E_2^*).

1.13. **Convergence factors of type I for multiple series.** The general term in a multiple series of order n may be identified by a set of subscripts $(i_1, i_2, \cdots, i_n)$. By way of abbreviation, we shall use the symbol $[i]$ to denote this set of subscripts. The series may then be represented by the notation $\sum u_{[i]}$. Using $[m]$ similarly in place of the set of symbols $(m_1, m_2, \cdots, m_n)$, we put

$$(35) \qquad\qquad s_{[m]} = \sum_{i_1=0}^{m_1} \sum_{i_2=0}^{m_2} \cdots \sum_{i_n=0}^{m_n} u_{[i]}.$$

We suppose that the multiple series in question is convergent and that we are given an n-tuply infinite set of functions

(36) $\qquad f_{i_1,i_2,\cdots,i_n}(\alpha)$ or $f_{[i]}$ $\qquad\qquad (i_k = 0, 1, 2, \cdots ; k = 1, 2, \cdots, n)$,

defined over a set of points $E(\alpha)$ of the type previously considered. We suppose further that the multiple series satisfies the condition

(37) $\qquad\qquad\qquad\qquad |s_{[m]}| < C$ $\qquad\qquad\qquad\qquad$ (all $[m]$),

where C is a positive constant. We wish to find necessary and sufficient conditions on the functions (36) in order that the series

(38) $\qquad\qquad\qquad\qquad \sum u_{[i]}f_{[i]}(\alpha)$

may converge in $E(\alpha)$ and satisfy for each α the condition analogous to (37).

We now introduce the notations

$$\Delta_{11\cdots1}f_{[i]} = \sum_{k_1=0}^{1}\sum_{k_2=0}^{1}\cdots\sum_{k_n=0}^{1}(-1)^{k_1}(-1)^{k_2}\cdots(-1)^{k_n}f_{[i+k]},$$

(39)

$$\Delta_{11\cdots10}f_{[i]} = \sum_{k_1=0}^{1}\sum_{k_2=0}^{1}\cdots\sum_{k_{n-1}=0}^{1}(-1)^{k_1}(-1)^{k_2}\cdots(-1)^{k_{n-1}}f_{i_1+k_1,\cdots,i_{n-1}+k_{n-1},i_n},$$

$$\cdots\cdots\cdots\cdots\cdots\cdots\cdots\cdots\cdots\cdots\cdots\cdots\cdots$$

$$\Delta_{10\cdots0}f_{[i]} = f_{i_1i_2\cdots i_n} - f_{i_1+1,i_2\cdots i_n},$$

with analogous conventions for the symbols Δ with zero subscripts in different positions.

We may then obtain from the generalization of the Abel transformation to multiple series

$$\sigma_{[m]}(\alpha) = \sum_{i_1=0}^{m_1}\cdots\sum_{i_n=0}^{m_n}u_{[i]}f_{[i]}(\alpha)$$

$$= \sum_{i_1=0}^{m_1-1}\cdots\sum_{i_n=0}^{m_n-1}s_{[i]}\Delta_{11\cdots1}f_{[i]}(\alpha)$$

(40)

$$+ \left[\sum_{i_1=0}^{m_1-1}\cdots\sum_{i_{n-1}=0}^{m_{n-1}-1}s_{[i,1,m]}\Delta_{11\cdots10}f_{[i,1,m]}(\alpha)\right] + \cdots$$

$$+ \left[\sum_{i_1=0}^{m_1-1}\cdots\sum_{i_{n-k}=0}^{m_{n-k}-1}s_{[i,k,m]}\Delta_{1\cdots10\cdots0}f_{[i,k,m]}(\alpha)\right] + \cdots$$

$$+ s_{[m]}f_{[m]}(\alpha),$$

where the small bracket symbol $[i, k, m]$, for $k = 1, 2, \cdots, n$, stands for the set of indices $i_1 \cdots i_{n-k}$, $m_{n-k+1} \cdots m_n$, and the large brackets inclosing an expression indicate the sum of the whole group of terms of similar form, obtained by permutation of indices.

The first term on the right hand side of (40) will converge to a limit in $E(\alpha)$ as the m's become infinite, provided

$(A)_n$ $$\sum_{i_1=0}^{\infty} \cdots \sum_{i_n=0}^{\infty} |\Delta_{11\ldots 1}f_{[i]}(\alpha)| < K(\alpha)$$ $E(\alpha),$

$K(\alpha)$ being a positive function of α.

Before introducing the conditions needed for the discussion of the other terms in (40) we find it convenient to define a further notation. We shall represent by

(41) $$\Delta_{1,0}^{n-k,k}$$

a Δ symbol having as subscripts $(n-k)$ unities and k zeros. We then add the following conditions:

  n conditions $(D_s^{(1)})$ of the type

$(D_1^{(1)})$ $$\lim_{i_n\to\infty} \Delta_{11\ldots 10}f_{[i]}(\alpha) = 0 \quad (E(\alpha); \text{ all } i_1, \cdots, i_{n-1}),$$

  $(2^n - n - 2)$ conditions $(D_s^{(k)})$ of the type

$(D_1^{(k)})$ $$\lim_{i_{n-k+1}\to\infty \cdots i_n\to\infty} \Delta_{1,0}^{n-k,k}f_{[i]}(\alpha) = 0 \quad (E(\alpha); \text{ all } i_1, \cdots, i_{n-k}),$$

k ranging from 2 to $(n-1)$ inclusive, and s from 1 to $\binom{n}{k}$ for each k.

From the conditions $(D_s^{(k)})$ we may infer that the Δ's on the left hand side will also approach zero as any subset of the indices occurring in the limit symbol become infinite, the remaining indices being held fixed. Before proceeding to this discussion we find it desirable to introduce an additional notation. For any expression $F_{[m]}$ depending on the indices $[m]$, we set

(42) $$\mathcal{D}^{k,p_k}\{F_{[m]}\} = F_{[m]} - F_{m_1\cdots m_{k-1}p_k m_{k+1}\cdots m_n}.$$

Then we have

$$\sum_{i_1=m_1}^{p_1-1} \Delta_{10\ldots 0}F_{[i,n-1,m]} = \mathcal{D}^{1,p_1}\{F_{[m]}\},$$

which, for the case $F_{[m]} = \Delta_{01\ldots 1}f_{[m]}$, yields

$$\mathcal{D}^{1,p_1}\{\Delta_{01\ldots 1}f_{[m]}\} = \sum_{i_1=m_1}^{p_1-1} \Delta_{11\ldots 1}f_{[i,n-1,m]}.$$

If we allow p_1 to become infinite, we obtain from this equation and one of the conditions $(D_s^{(1)})$

(43) $$\sum_{i_1=m_1}^{\infty} \Delta_{11\ldots 1}f_{[i,n-1,m]} = \Delta_{01\ldots 1}f_{[m]}.$$

  From (43) we have

$$\sum_{i_2=m_2}^{p_2-1} \sum_{i_1=m_1}^{\infty} \Delta_{11\ldots 1}f_{[i,n-2,m]} = \mathcal{D}^{2,p_2}\{\Delta_{001\ldots 1}f_{[m]}\},$$

whence

$$\Delta_{001\ldots 1}f_{[m]} = \sum_{i_2=m_2}^{p_2-1} \sum_{i_1=m_1}^{\infty} \Delta_{11\ldots 1}f_{[i,n-2,m]} + \Delta_{001\ldots 1}f_{m_1 p_2 m_3\cdots m_n}.$$

In view of condition $(A)_n$ we can make the first term on the right hand side of this equation uniformly small for all m_2 and p_2 by taking m_1 sufficiently large. From the appropriate condition of the type $(D_s^{(2)})$ we see that the second term on the right hand side can be made small by choosing m_1 and p_2 sufficiently large. Hence the left hand side can be made small by choosing m_1 sufficiently large, the remaining m's being held fixed. Similarly it can be shown that the same expression can be made small by choosing m_2 sufficiently large, the other m's being held fixed.

We have

$$\sum_{i_1=m_1}^{p_1-1} \sum_{i_2=m_2}^{p_2-1} \Delta_{11\ldots1}f_{[i,\,n-2,\,m]} = \mathcal{D}^{1,\,p_1}\mathcal{D}^{2,\,p_2}\{\Delta_{001\ldots1}f_{[m]}\} \, .$$

Allowing p_1 and p_2 to become infinite and making use of the results just proved, we obtain

$$(44) \qquad\qquad \sum_{i_1=m_1}^{\infty} \sum_{i_2=m_2}^{\infty} \Delta_{11\ldots1}f_{[i,\,n-2,\,m]} = \Delta_{001\ldots1}f_{[m]} \, .$$

From this equation, by a discussion analogous to that carried through above in connection with equation (43), we may show that

$$(45) \qquad\qquad \Delta_{0001\ldots1}f_{[m]}$$

will tend to zero when m_1 and m_2 become infinite, the other m's being held fixed. To show the same thing for any other combination of two of the three indices m_1, m_2, m_3, we start with the analogue of (44), which has the m's in question occurring on the left hand side in place of m_1 and m_2.

To deal with the case where only one of the three indices m_1, m_2, m_3, becomes infinite, we obtain from (43) the relation

$$\sum_{i_3=m_3}^{p_3-1} \sum_{i_2=m_2}^{p_2-1} \sum_{i_1=m_1}^{\infty} \Delta_{11\ldots1}f_{[i,\,n-3,\,m]} = \sum_{i_3=m_3}^{p_3-1} \sum_{i_2=m_2}^{p_2-1} \Delta_{01\ldots1}f_{[m]}$$
$$= \mathcal{D}^{2,\,p_2}\mathcal{D}^{3,\,p_3}\{\Delta_{0001\ldots1}f_{[m]}\} \, .$$

From this we obtain by expanding the right hand side and transposing

$$\Delta_{0001\ldots1}f_{[m]} = \sum_{i_3=m_3}^{p_3-1} \sum_{i_2=m_2}^{p_2-1} \sum_{i_1=m_1}^{\infty} \Delta_{11\ldots1}f_{[i,\,n-3,\,m]}$$
$$+ \Delta_{0001\ldots1}f_{m_1 p_2 m_3 \cdots m_n} + \Delta_{0001\ldots1}f_{m_1 m_2 p_3 m_4 \cdots m_n} - \Delta_{0001\ldots1}f_{m_1 p_2 p_3 m_4 \cdots m_n} \, .$$

The first term on the right hand side of the above equation tends to zero uniformly in m_2, m_3, p_2, p_3, as m_1 becomes infinite, as we see from condition $(A)_n$. By the appropriate condition of the form $(D_s^{(3)})$ we see that the last term tends to zero as m_1, p_2, and p_3 become infinite. By what we have previously shown with regard to the behavior of (45) when two of the indices become infinite, we see that the second and third terms tend to zero as m_1 and p_2 or m_1 and p_3, respectively, become infinite. Hence it follows that the left hand side of the last equation tends to zero as $m_1 \to \infty$, the other indices being held fixed.

By continuing the argument developed above in the case of the Δ's with two or three zeros among their indices, we can demonstrate that any of the Δ's occurring in the conditions $(D_s^{(k)})$ will tend to zero as any combination of the i's, chosen from those corresponding to the zero indices of the Δ's, become infinite. In the course of this discussion we incidentally establish a set of $\binom{n}{k}$ equations of the form

$$(46) \qquad \sum_{i_1=m_1}^{\infty} \cdots \sum_{i_k=m_k}^{\infty} \Delta_{11\ldots1} f_{[i,n-k,m]} = \Delta_{0,1}^{k,n-k} f_{[m]}.$$

From (37), condition $(A)_n$, and equations of the type (46) we can infer that each term in brackets on the right hand side of (40) tends to zero as the m's become infinite. Since there is a fixed number of these terms, it follows that their sum tends to zero under the same conditions.

We consider next the last term on the right hand side of (40). If we take equation (46) for the case where $k = n - 1$ and $m_1 = m_2 = \cdots = m_{n-1} = 0$, allow the index m_n to take on the values $0, 1, 2, \cdots, m_n - 1$, and sum, we obtain by the use of condition $(A)_n$:

$$| f_{0\ldots00}(\alpha) - f_{0\ldots0m_n}(\alpha) | < K(\alpha) \qquad\qquad E(\alpha).$$

A similar discussion yields the inequalities

$$| f_{0\ldots0m_n}(\alpha) - f_{0\ldots m_{n-1}m_n}(\alpha) | < K(\alpha), \cdots,$$

$$| f_{0\ldots0m_k\cdots m_n}(\alpha) - f_{0\ldots0m_{k-1}m_k\cdots m_n}(\alpha) | < K(\alpha), \cdots,$$

$$| f_{0m_2\cdots m_n}(\alpha) - f_{m_1m_2\cdots m_n}(\alpha) | < K(\alpha).$$

From these inequalities we readily infer that, for each α in $E(\alpha)$, $f_{[m]}(\alpha)$ remains bounded for all $[m]$. Hence the last term on the right hand side of (40) will tend to zero as the m's become infinite, provided $s_{[m]}$ tends to zero under the same conditions. But any convergent series may be reduced to this case by alteration of the term $u_{00\ldots0}$, so we may conclude that the series (38) will converge whenever $\sum u_{[i]}$ converges and satisfies (37), and the factors (36) satisfy conditions $(A)_n$ and $(D_s^{(k)})$ $(k = 1, 2, \cdots, n)$. It is also readily seen that under the same conditions the partial sums of (38) remain bounded for all $[m]$ when α is fixed. Thus the sufficiency of our conditions for convergence factors of type I has been proved.

1.14. Necessity of the conditions. Consider first condition $(A)_n$. If this condition does not hold for a particular choice of α, α_1, we can select a set of values of p, differing by at least 2, $p_1, p_2, \cdots, p_m, \cdots$, such that if we define

$$\tau_p = \sum_{i_1=0}^{p} \sum_{i_2=0}^{p} \cdots \sum_{i_n=0}^{p} | \Delta_{11\ldots1} f_{[i]}(\alpha_1) |,$$

we shall have

$$\tau_{p_{l+1}} - \tau_{p_l+1} > 1 \qquad\qquad (l = 1, 2, 3, \cdots).$$

We may then obtain a contradiction from the identity (40) by using the special series for which

$$s_{[i]} = \{\operatorname{sgn} \Delta_{11\cdots1} f_{[i]}(\alpha_1)\} m^{-1} \left. \begin{array}{l} 0 \leq i_k \leq p_{m+1} \\ \qquad (k = 1, 2, \cdots, r) \\ p_m + 1 < i_{r+1} \leq p_{m+1} \\ 0 \leq i_k \leq p_m + 1 \\ \qquad (k = r + 2, \cdots, n) \end{array} \right\} (r = n - 2, n - 3, \cdots, 1),$$

and also when the first inequality is omitted and $r = 0$ in the other two, or the last inequality is omitted and $r = (n - 1)$ in the other two;

$$s_{[i]} = 0 \qquad\qquad \text{(all other } [i]\text{)}.$$

For, under our hypotheses, the left hand side of (40) will tend to a limit as the m's become infinite in any manner, whereas the right hand side becomes infinite if the m's become infinite by each taking on the special set of values $p_2 + 1$, $p_3 + 1$, $\cdots$. The necessity of $(A)_n$ is therefore established.

The proofs of the necessity of the various conditions $(D_s^{(k)})$ are all analogous, so we shall carry through the discussion for one typical case only.

If $(D_1^{(k)})$ does not hold for a particular value of α, α_1, and a particular set of values $p_1, p_2, \cdots, p_{n-k}$, of the indices $i_1, i_2, \cdots, i_{n-k}$, we can find an $\epsilon > 0$ such that

$$|\Delta_{1,0}^{n-k,k} f_{[i]}(\alpha_1)| > \epsilon \{i_r = p_r(r = 1, \cdots, n - k); i_r = q_r^{(j)}(r = n - k + 1, \cdots, n)\},$$

for an infinite number of choices of the q's, $q_r^{(1)}, q_r^{(2)}, \cdots (r = n - k + 1, \cdots, n)$, where each of a new set of q's exceeds the corresponding one of the previous set by at least 2. We then consider the series for which

$$s_{p_1 \cdots p_{n-k} q_{n-k+1}^{(j)} \cdots q_n^{(j)}} = (-1)^j [\operatorname{sgn} \Delta_{1,0}^{n-k,k} f_{[i]}(\alpha_1)] \qquad (j = 1, 2, \cdots),$$

where the indices i of f take on the values of the indices of s,

$$s_{[i]} = 0 \qquad\qquad \text{(all other choices of } [i]\text{)}.$$

This series converges to the value zero and satisfies condition (37). If in the identity (40) we allow the indices $[m]$ to become infinite in such a manner that $m_r = q_r^{(j)}(r = n - k + 1, \cdots, n; j = 1, 2, \cdots)$, while $m_r > p_r (r = 1, 2, \cdots, n - k)$, one term on the right hand side of (40) will oscillate between values $> \epsilon$ and $< - \epsilon$. The other terms on the right hand side, and the left hand side, will approach definite limits. This contradiction establishes the necessity of $(D_1^{(k)})$, and as stated before the proof of the necessity of any other condition of this type is analogous.

We have now completely established the following theorem:

THEOREM VII. *The necessary and sufficient conditions that the series* (38) *converge in* $E(\alpha)$, *and that for each* α *its partial sums,* $\sigma_{[m]}(\alpha)$ *remain bounded for all* $[m]$, *whenever the series* (35) *is convergent and satisfies* (37), *are that the functions* (36) *satisfy* $(A)_n$ *and the conditions* $(D_s^{(k)})$, *where* k *ranges from* 1 *to* $(n - 1)$ *and, for each* k, s *ranges from* 1 *to* $\binom{n}{k}$.

1.15. Sequence to function transformations for multiple sequences. Given any convergent multiple sequence

$$(47) \qquad\qquad s_{[i]} \qquad\qquad (i_1, i_2, \cdots, i_n = 0, 1, 2, \cdots),$$

which satisfies condition (37), and a set of functions

$$(48) \qquad\qquad \varphi_{[i]}(\alpha) \qquad\qquad (i_1, i_2, \cdots, i_n = 0, 1, 2, \cdots),$$

defined over the set $E(\alpha)$, we seek necessary and sufficient conditions that the series

$$(49) \qquad\qquad \sum_{i_1=0}^{\infty} \cdots \sum_{i_n=0}^{\infty} s_{[i]} \varphi_{[i]}(\alpha)$$

should converge in $E(\alpha)$.   From the special case

$$s_{[i]} = 1 \qquad\qquad (i_1 \geqq m_1, \cdots, i_n \geqq m_n; m_1, \cdots, m_n = 0, 1, 2, \cdots),$$

$$s_{[i]} = 0 \qquad\qquad (i_1 < m_1 \text{ or } i_2 < m_2 \text{ or } \cdots \text{ or } i_n < m_n),$$

we see that we may define a set of functions $f_{[m]}(\alpha)$ by the equations

$$(50) \qquad f_{[m]}(\alpha) = \sum_{i_1=m_1}^{\infty} \cdots \sum_{i_n=m_n}^{\infty} \varphi_{[i]}(\alpha) \qquad\qquad (m_1, \cdots, m_n = 0, 1, 2, \cdots),$$

since the series on the right hand side must converge in $E(\alpha)$ if (49) converges for all convergent $s_{[i]}$.   Furthermore, by a suitable choice of the s's as either unity or zero, depending on the indices, we may infer that any multiple series of lower order of multiplicity than n, chosen from (50) by holding one or more of the indices of $\varphi_{[i]}$ constant, the others ranging as in (50), will converge in $E(\alpha)$.

We then obtain from (50) and (46)

$$(51) \qquad \Delta_{11 \cdots 1} f_{[m]} = \varphi_{[m]}, \qquad \Delta_{0,1}^{k, n-k} f_{[m]} = \sum_{i_1=m_1}^{\infty} \cdots \sum_{i_k=m_k}^{\infty} \varphi_{[m]},$$

and a set of equations analogous to the second equation of (51), in which the zero subscripts of Δ occupy different positions.

If we define the series $\sum u_{[i]}$ in terms of the sequence $s_{[i]}$ by means of (35), we may use the identity (40) and the relationships (51) to express

$$(52) \qquad\qquad \sum_{i_1=0}^{m_1-1} \cdots \sum_{i_n=0}^{m_n-1} s_{[i]} \varphi_{[i]}(\alpha)$$

in the form $\sigma_{[m]}(\alpha)$ minus the terms on the right hand side of (40) subsequent to the first.

Condition $(A)_n$ of the necessary and sufficient conditions for the convergence of $\sigma_{[m]}(\alpha)$ may, in view of the first equation in (51), be written in the form

$$(A^*)_n \qquad\qquad \sum_{i_1=0}^{\infty} \cdots \sum_{i_n=0}^{\infty} |\varphi_{[i]}(\alpha)| < K(\alpha) \qquad\qquad E(\alpha).$$

From the second equation in (51) and other equations of this type we see that condition $(A^*)_n$ implies that the functions $f_{[m]}(\alpha)$, defined by (50), satisfy all the conditions $(D_s^{(k)})$. Hence $(A^*)_n$ is the necessary and sufficient condition for the approach to a limit of $\sigma_{[m]}(\alpha)$ as the m's become infinite. It is obviously a sufficient condition for the convergence of (52) and may readily be proved necessary as well. The proof is entirely analogous to the discussion of the necessity of the corresponding condition $(A^*)_2$ in 1.9. Since $(A^*)_n$ implies the conditions $(D_s^{(k)})$, we see that it is sufficient that all the terms on the right hand side of (40) after the first and before the last, tend to zero as the m's become infinite. If we take account of (50) we can infer the same thing for the last term on the right hand side of (40). Hence $(A^*)_n$ is sufficient that (52) tend to the same limit as $\sigma_{[m]}(\alpha)$. It is also necessary for this purpose, since it is necessary for the convergence of (52).

We have then this result:

LEMMA 3. *The necessary and sufficient condition that the series* (52) *converge in* $E(\alpha)$ *for any convergent sequence, satisfying* (37), *is that the functions* (48) *satisfy* $(A^*)_n$. *This condition is also necessary and sufficient that the value of* (52) *shall be the same as that of the related series with convergence factors,* (38).

1.16. **Convergence factors of type II for multiple series.** We turn next to the case where each of the functions (36) tends to a limit as α approaches a limit point, α_0, not in $E(\alpha)$. For an $s_{[i]}$ which tends to zero as the i's become infinite, and a set of convergence factors which satisfy $(A)_n$ and the various conditions $(D_s^{(k)})$ we obtain from (40) by allowing the m's to become infinite

$$(53) \qquad \sum_{i_1=0}^{\infty} \cdots \sum_{i_n=0}^{\infty} u_{[i]} f_{[i]}(\alpha) = \sum_{i_1=0}^{\infty} \cdots \sum_{i_n=0}^{\infty} s_{[i]} \Delta_{11\ldots1} f_{[i]}(\alpha).$$

If we add to the conditions on the $f_{[i]}(\alpha)$ the following:

n conditions $(E_s)_n$ of the type

$$(E_1)_n \qquad\qquad \lim_{\alpha\to\alpha_0} \left\{ \sum_{i_2=0}^{\infty} \cdots \sum_{i_n=0}^{\infty} |\Delta_{11\ldots1} f_{[i]}(\alpha)| \right\} = 0 \qquad (i_1 = 0, 1, 2, \cdots),$$

$$(C)_n \qquad\qquad \lim_{\alpha\to\alpha_0} f_{[i]}(\alpha) = 1 \qquad\qquad (\text{all } [i]),$$

we see that the right hand side of (53) will tend to zero as α approaches α_0, for an $s_{[i]}$ satisfying (37) and approaching zero as the i's become infinite, provided $\sum |\Delta_{11\ldots1} f_{[i]}(\alpha)|$ remains uniformly bounded in a certain neighborhood of α_0. We therefore add the requirement

$$(A_1)_n \qquad\qquad \sum_{i_1=0}^{\infty} \cdots \sum_{i_n=0}^{\infty} |\Delta_{11\ldots1} f_{[i]}(\alpha)| < K \qquad\qquad E'(\alpha),$$

where $E'(\alpha)$ contains all the points of $E(\alpha)$ lying in a certain neighborhood of α_0, and K is a positive constant. Thus we see that conditions $(A)_n$, $(A_1)_n$, $(D_s^{(k)})$, $(E_s)_n$, and $(C)_n$ are sufficient for convergence factors of type II in the case where the given series converges to zero. Since the general case reduces readily to this special case, the sufficiency of the conditions may be regarded as proved in general.

1.17. Necessity of the conditions. The necessity of $(A)_n$ and the various conditions $(D_s^{(k)})$ has been proved in 1.14. The proofs of the necessity of $(C)_n$, $(A_1)_n$, and $(E_s)_n$ are analogous to the proofs of the necessity of (C) in 1.5, of $(A_1)_2$ in 1.11, and of (E_1) and (E_2) in 1.11.

We thus have the following theorem:

THEOREM VIII. *The necessary and sufficient conditions that the series* (38) *converge in $E(\alpha)$ and for each α have its partial sums bounded, whenever the series* (35) *converges and satisfies* (37), *and approach the value of* (35) *when α approaches α_0, are that the functions* (36) *satisfy* $(A)_n$, $(A_1)_n$, $(C)_n$, *the conditions* $(D_s^{(k)})$, *and the conditions* $(E_s)_n$.

1.18. Applications of sequence to function transformations in the case of multiple sequences. In 1.12 we obtained from Theorem V the necessary and sufficient conditions that the evaluation of a double series by means of a double sequence to function transformation should yield the appropriate value in the case of a convergent double series satisfying (15). In a similar manner we can obtain from Theorem VIII the necessary and sufficient conditions for the regularity of a method of evaluating a multiple series by a sequence to function transformation.

We know from Lemma 3 that $(A^*)_n$ is the necessary and sufficient condition that (52) converge in $E(\alpha)$, and that under this condition we have the identity

$$(54) \qquad \sum_{i_1=0}^{\infty} \cdots \sum_{i_n=0}^{\infty} s_{[i]}\, \varphi_{[i]}(\alpha) = \sum_{i_1=0}^{\infty} \cdots \sum_{i_n=0}^{\infty} u_{[i]} f_{[i]}(\alpha),$$

$\sum u_{[i]}$ being the multiple series from which the multiple sequence $s_{[i]}$ is obtained by means of (35), and the $f_{[i]}(\alpha)$ being the functions defined by (50) and therefore related also to the $\varphi_{[i]}(\alpha)$ in the manner specified in (51). Hence the necessary and sufficient conditions that the left hand side of (54) should approach s, the limit of $s_{[i]}$, may be found by expressing the necessary and sufficient conditions of Theorem VIII in terms of the $\varphi_{[i]}(\alpha)$.

We have already seen that $(A^*)_n$ is equivalent to $(A)_n$ and the various conditions $(D_s^{(k)})$. From (51) we infer that $(A_1)_n$ is equivalent to

$$(A_1^*)_n \qquad\qquad \sum_{i_1=0}^{\infty} \cdots \sum_{i_n=0}^{\infty} |\varphi_{[i]}(\alpha)| < K \qquad\qquad E'(\alpha),$$

and that conditions $(E_s)_n$ of the form $(E_1)_n$ are equivalent to conditions $(E_s^*)_n$ of the form

$$(E_1^*)_n \qquad \lim_{\alpha \to \alpha_0} \left\{ \sum_{i_2=0}^{\infty} \cdots \sum_{i_n=0}^{\infty} | \varphi_{[i]}(\alpha) | \right\} = 0 \qquad (i_1 = 0, 1, 2, \cdots).$$

From $(C)_n$ and (50) we obtain

$$(C^*)_n \qquad \lim_{\alpha \to \alpha_0} \sum_{i_1=0}^{\infty} \cdots \sum_{i_n=0}^{\infty} \varphi_{[i]}(\alpha) = 1,$$

and from this condition and conditions $(E_s^*)_n$ we can derive $(C)_n$.

We thus have the result:

THEOREM IX. *The necessary and sufficient conditions that the limit of (52) as α approaches α_0 shall be s, for every sequence $s_{[i]}$ satisfying (37) and converging to s, are that the functions (48) satisfy $(A^*)_n$, $(A_1^*)_n$, $(C^*)_n$, and the n conditions $(E_s^*)_n$.*

1.19. Convergence factors of type I for completely convergent double series. If a convergent double series has each of its rows and columns convergent, we shall say that it is completely convergent.[15] If the series $\sum u_{ij} f_{ij}(\alpha)$ is completely convergent whenever the series $\sum u_{ij}$ has that property, we shall say that the functions $f_{ij}(\alpha)$ are convergence factors of type I for completely convergent double series. We seek necessary and sufficient conditions for this case. Theorem IV suggests the requirement that the functions $f_{ij}(\alpha)$ satisfy condition $(A)_2$ of that theorem. Applying Theorem I to the first column and first row of our double series, we are led to impose the conditions

$$(A^{(1)}) \qquad \sum_{i=0}^{\infty} | \Delta_{10} f_{i0}(\alpha) | < K_1(\alpha) \qquad\qquad E(\alpha),$$

$$(A^{(2)}) \qquad \sum_{j=0}^{\infty} | \Delta_{01} f_{0j}(\alpha) | < K_2(\alpha) \qquad\qquad E(\alpha),$$

where $K_1(\alpha)$ and $K_2(\alpha)$ are positive functions of α. We need of course conditions analogous to $(A^{(1)})$ and $(A^{(2)})$ to derive the desired properties for the other columns and rows of $\sum u_{ij} f_{ij}(\alpha)$. We find, however, that such conditions may be obtained as a consequence of $(A^{(1)})$, $(A^{(2)})$, and $(A)_2$. We shall thus derive the conditions for the other columns, noting that those for the other rows may be obtained in analogous fashion. We have from (19)

$$(55) \qquad \sum_{j=0}^{n-1} \Delta_{11} f_{ij}(\alpha) = \Delta_{10} f_{i0}(\alpha) - \Delta_{10} f_{in}(\alpha),$$

whence it follows that

$$(56) \quad \begin{aligned} \sum_{i=0}^{\infty} | \Delta_{10} f_{in}(\alpha) | &\leq \sum_{i=0}^{\infty} | \Delta_{10} f_{i0}(\alpha) | + \sum_{i=0}^{\infty} | \Delta_{10} f_{in}(\alpha) - \Delta_{10} f_{i0}(\alpha) | \\ &< K_1(\alpha) + \sum_{i=0}^{\infty} \sum_{j=0}^{n-1} | \Delta_{11} f_{ij}(\alpha) | < K_1(\alpha) + K(\alpha) \qquad (n = 1, 2, 3, \cdots). \end{aligned}$$

---

[15] G. H. Hardy [66] has utilized the term "regularly convergent" to characterize this property. Since the word "regular" is used in another connection in this work, we have preferred the terminology above.

We may therefore conclude from Theorem I that all the columns of $\sum u_{ij} f_{ij}(\alpha)$ are convergent in $E(\alpha)$. As indicated above, an analogous argument serves to establish the convergence of the rows.

Equation (55) and condition (A)$_2$ enable us to infer the uniform convergence of

$$\sum_{i=0}^{\infty} | \Delta_{10} f_{iq}(\alpha) |$$

for all q, α being fixed. An analogous argument yields the uniform convergence of

$$\sum_{j=0}^{\infty} | \Delta_{01} f_{pj}(\alpha) |$$

for all p. Thus we can conclude that the second and third terms on the right hand side of (20) tend to limits as p and q become infinite, whenever $\sum u_{ij}$ is completely convergent.

From condition $(A^{(1)})$ we conclude that $f_{p0}(\alpha)$ tends to a limit as p becomes infinite and from condition $(A^{(2)})$ we infer that $f_{0q}(\alpha)$ tends to a limit as q becomes infinite. Since

$$\sum_{i=0}^{p-1} \sum_{j=0}^{q-1} \Delta_{11} f_{ij}(\alpha) = f_{00}(\alpha) - f_{p0}(\alpha) - f_{0q}(\alpha) + f_{pq}(\alpha),$$

we may use (A)$_2$ and the results indicated above to conclude that $f_{pq}(\alpha)$ tends to a limit as p and q become infinite. Therefore the last term on the right hand side of (20) tends to a limit as p and q become infinite, whenever the series $\sum u_{ij}$ is completely convergent.

The approach to a limit of the first term on the right hand side of (20) follows from (A)$_2$. Thus we see that when the functions $f_{ij}(\alpha)$ satisfy conditions (A)$_2$, $(A^{(1)})$, and $(A^{(2)})$, the right hand side of (20) tends to a limit whenever $\sum u_{ij}$ is completely convergent. Thus the convergence of $\sum u_{ij} f_{ij}(\alpha)$ is established, and since we have previously shown that its rows and columns converge, we have proved the sufficiency of our conditions for the complete convergence of this series.

Since the series used to show the necessity of (A)$_2$ in 1.8 are completely convergent, it follows that (A)$_2$ is necessary in the present instance. It follows from the necessity of (A) in Theorem I that $(A^{(1)})$ and $(A^{(2)})$ are necessary for the complete convergence of $\sum u_{ij} f_{ij}(\alpha)$. We thus have the theorem:

THEOREM X. *The necessary and sufficient conditions that the series $\sum u_{ij} f_{ij}(\alpha)$ converge completely whenever the series $\sum u_{ij}$ converges completely, are that the convergence factors $f_{ij}(\alpha)$ satisfy* (A)$_2$, $(A^{(1)})$, *and* $(A^{(2)})$.

We would naturally expect that since we have placed more restrictions on the series $\sum u_{ij}$ in Theorem X than in Theorem IV, the conditions on the convergence factors might be somewhat less stringent in the present instance. That this is actually the case is readily seen. For, by using equations (21) which result from (D$_1$) and (D$_2$), we may readily infer $(A^{(1)})$ and $(A^{(2)})$ by use of

$(A)_2$. Thus any set of convergence factors which satisfy $(A)_2$, (D_1), and (D_2), will also satisfy $(A^{(1)})$ and $(A^{(2)})$. It can be shown by an example, however, that there exist sets of convergence factors satisfying $(A)_2$, $(A^{(1)})$, and $(A^{(2)})$, which do not satisfy (D_1) or (D_2). For this purpose we set

$$f_{ij}(\alpha) = \left(1 + \frac{\beta}{i}\right)\left(1 + \frac{\gamma}{j}\right),$$

the set $E(\alpha)$ being defined by the inequalities, $\beta > 0, \gamma > 0$.

1.20. Convergence factors of type I for completely convergent multiple series.
Suppose that we have a convergent multiple series of order n such that any simple series obtained from it by holding all the subscripts of the terms but one fixed, while allowing that one to vary as in the multiple series, is convergent. Suppose further that any multiple series of lower order than n obtained from the given multiple series by holding a certain set of the subscripts fixed, while allowing the remaining subscripts to vary as in the given series, is convergent. We then say that the multiple series of order n is completely convergent. If we have a set of convergence factors $f_{[i]}(\alpha)$ such that the series $\sum u_{[i]}f_{[i]}(\alpha)$ is completely convergent whenever the series $\sum u_{[i]}$ has this property, we designate the $f_{[i]}(\alpha)$ as convergence factors of type I for completely convergent multiple series. We seek necessary and sufficient conditions for this case.

By analogy with the results of Theorem X we are led to retain condition $(A)_n$ of Theorem VII and replace conditions $(D_s^{(k)})$ of that theorem by conditions $(A_s^{(k)})$ of the form

$$(A_1^{(k)}) \quad \sum_{i_1=0}^{\infty} \cdots \sum_{i_{n-k}=0}^{\infty} |\Delta_{1,0}^{n-k,k} f_{[i]}(\alpha)| < K_1^k(\alpha) \quad (E(\alpha); i_{n-k+1} = 0, \cdots, i_n = 0),$$

where k ranges from 1 to $n - 1$, for each k, s ranges from 1 to $\binom{n}{k}$, and the various functions $K_s^{(k)}(\alpha)$ are positive functions of α.

The various conditions $(A_s^{(k)})$ are sufficient for the convergence of the corresponding multiple series chosen from $\sum u_{[i]}$, where the fixed indices are each equal to zero. To deal with other choices we obtain from (46)

$$(57) \quad \sum_{i_1=0}^{\infty} \cdots \sum_{i_k=0}^{\infty} \sum_{i_{k+1}=0}^{m_{k+1}-1} \cdots \sum_{i_{k+j}=0}^{m_{k+j}-1} \Delta_{11\cdots 1} f_{[i]}$$
$$= \mathcal{D}^{k+1,m_{k+1}} \cdots \mathcal{D}^{k+j,m_{k+j}} \{\Delta_{0,1}^{k+j,n-k-j} f_{[i]}\} \quad (i_1 = 0, \cdots, i_{k+j} = 0).$$

By combining equations of this type with $(A)_n$ and suitably chosen conditions of the form $(A_s^{(k)})$ we obtain inequalities sufficient to establish the convergence of all the various multiple series chosen from $\sum u_{[i]}$.

Equations of the type (57), combined with condition $(A)_n$, enable us to infer the uniform convergence of series of the type

$$\sum_{i_1=0}^{\infty} \cdots \sum_{i_k=0}^{\infty} \Delta_{1,0}^{k,n-k} f_{[i,n-k,m]}$$

for all choices of the indices m. Thus we may conclude that the terms on the right hand side of (40), inclosed in brackets, tend to limits as the m's become infinite. The convergence of the first term on the right hand side of (40) follows from $(A)_n$. Conditions $(A_s^{(k)})$, combined with condition $(A)_n$, imply the approach to a limit of $f_{[m]}$ as the m's become infinite and hence the approach to a limit, under the same conditions, of the last term on the right hand side of (40). Thus we have shown the sufficiency of conditions $(A)_n$ and $(A_s^{(k)})$ for the complete convergence of $\sum u_{[i]} f_{[i]}(\alpha)$, whenever $\sum u_{[i]}$ is completely convergent.

The necessity of the conditions may be proved by induction. If we take the case $n = 3$, the necessity of the various conditions of type $(A_s^{(k)})$ follows from Theorem X. The necessity of condition $(A)_3$ follows from the proof of its necessity in Theorem VII, since the multiple series used in that proof were completely convergent. Assuming that the necessity of the conditions has been proved for $n = r$, we can pass to the case $n = r + 1$ in the same manner that we passed from $n = 2$ to $n = 3$. We thus have the theorem:

THEOREM XI. *The necessary and sufficient conditions that the series $\sum u_{[i]} f_{[i]}(\alpha)$ shall be completely convergent whenever $\sum u_{[i]}$ is completely convergent, are that the convergence factors $f_{[i]}(\alpha)$ satisfy $(A)_n$ and the various conditions $(A_s^{(k)})$.*

1.21. **Historical summary.** The theorems of the present chapter have many applications in the theory of infinite series, and particularly in questions concerning the regularity of definitions of the sum of a divergent series. As a consequence, most of them have reached the general form given here by a process of evolution. I shall make no attempt to outline this process in detail, but will confine myself in general to citing the various places where the theorems have been given in approximately definitive form.

Theorem I was first formulated and proved by Hadamard [56] in 1903. As indicated in the paper referred to, the result traces back to a famous lemma of Abel [1], which may be regarded as the germ of all the theorems of this chapter. The sufficiency proof for Theorem II was given by Carmichael [29] in 1918 and Perron [129] in 1920. The same conditions (with a redundant condition included) were proved necessary and sufficient by Takenaka [154] in 1922. In all these cases, as in the case of most theorems for convergence factors of type II found in the literature, a special set of points $E(\alpha)$ and a particular limit point α_0 were utilized. This does not affect the general nature of the proof but it does restrict the domain where the theorems may be applied directly without a change of variable. The more general form of statement was introduced by Moore [118] (cf. also [119]) in 1914 in connection with a modification and application of a convergence factor theorem due to Bromwich. The sufficiency of the conditions of Theorem III was obtained by Silverman [147] in 1910 (publication in 1913) for a transformation of finite range of particular importance. Necessity and sufficiency were proved by Toeplitz [156] in 1913 for a somewhat more general case and by Schur [145] in 1920 for a transformation of infinite range with a particular $E(\alpha)$ and α_0.

Theorems IV and V for the case where the set $E(\alpha)$ is two-dimensional are contained in results published by Moore [121] in 1927. Theorm VI for a particular $E(\alpha)$ and α_0 is contained in results given by Hamilton [60] in 1936. This paper contains a very complete study of the conditions under which various properties of multiple sequences are preserved or modified by transformations of a general type. In §1.8 of the paper a résumé of earlier literature is given containing references to results of Kojima [96] and Robison [139] related to Theorem VI. Theorems VII and VIII for the case where $E(\alpha)$ is n-dimensional for an n-tuple series were given by Moore [121] in 1927. Theorem IX for a particular $E(\alpha)$ and α_0 is contained in the paper by Hamilton [60] referred to above. Theorem X was given by Hardy [66] in 1917 and Theorem XI was suggested, but not explicitly formulated, in the same paper.

CHAPTER II

SUMMATION OF SERIES BY NÖRLUND MEANS

2.1. Definitions. We are given an infinite set of complex constants, $c_0 \neq 0$, c_1, c_2, $\cdots$, c_n, $\cdots$, and we set

$$(1) \qquad C_n = c_0 + c_1 + c_2 + \cdots + c_n.$$

For any series $\sum u_n$, where $s_n = \sum_{i=0}^{i=n} u_i$, we form

$$(2) \qquad \sigma_n = \frac{c_0 s_n + c_1 s_{n-1} + \cdots + c_n s_0}{C_n} = \frac{S_n}{C_n}.$$

If $\sigma_n \to \sigma$ as $n \to \infty$, we say that the series $\sum u_n$ is summable $(N; c)$ to the value σ.

2.2. Regularity of the definition. We now make use of Theorem III of Chapter I to determine the conditions under which the definition of the preceding section yields the appropriate value when applied to any convergent series. We have in this case for the $\varphi_n(\alpha)$ of Theorem III (I)

$$(3) \qquad \begin{aligned} \varphi_n(m) &= \frac{c_{m-n}}{C_m} & (0 \leq n \leq m), \\[2mm] \varphi_n(m) &= 0 & (n > m). \end{aligned}$$

The $E(\alpha)$ corresponds to the range $m = 0, 1, 2, \cdots$, and $\alpha_0 = +\infty$.

It is obvious from the definitions (3) that (A*) and (C$_2$) are satisfied in all cases. Condition (A$_1^*$) is equivalent to

$$(4) \qquad \sum_{k=0}^{m} |c_k| < H|C_m| \qquad \begin{pmatrix} H \text{ a positive constant,} \\ m = 0, 1, 2, \cdots \end{pmatrix},$$

and condition (C$_1$) is equivalent to the statement that the right hand side of the first equation in (3) tends to zero as m becomes infinite. For the case in which $C_m \to \infty$ with m, which is the case of genuine interest, this latter condition may by the use of (4) be replaced by the simpler form

$$(5) \qquad \lim_{m \to \infty} \frac{c_m}{C_m} = 0.$$

For set

$$(6) \qquad g_m = |c_m|, \quad G_m = g_0 + g_1 + \cdots + g_m \quad (m = 0, 1, 2, \cdots).$$

It follows from (5) that, corresponding to any $\epsilon > 0$, we can find p_1 such that

$$\left| \frac{c_q}{C_q} \right| < \frac{\epsilon}{H} \qquad (q \geq p_1).$$

We then choose p_2 such that

$$\left|\frac{c_k}{C_q}\right| < \epsilon \qquad \begin{pmatrix} k = 0, 1, 2, \cdots, p_1 - 1 \\ q \geqq p_2 \geqq p_1 \end{pmatrix}.$$

For $q \geqq k \geqq p_1$, we have

$$\left|\frac{c_k}{C_q}\right| = \left|\frac{c_k}{C_k}\right| \cdot \left|\frac{C_k}{C_q}\right| < \left|\frac{c_k}{C_k}\right| \cdot \frac{G_k}{G_q/H} \leqq H \left|\frac{c_k}{C_k}\right| < \epsilon.$$

A combination of the last two inequalities shows that the $\varphi_n(m)$ defined by (3), will tend to zero for each n when m becomes infinite.

We thus have the result:[16]

THEOREM I.   *The necessary and sufficient conditions that the definition $(N; c)$ of 2.1 shall be regular are that (4) should subsist and that the right hand side of the first equation in (3) should tend to zero as $m \to \infty$. For the case where $C_m \to \infty$ as $m \to \infty$, (4) and (5) serve as necessary and sufficient conditions.*

2.3. **Double series.**   The generalization of Nörlund means to double series may be defined in the following fashion.   Given a doubly infinite set of complex constants $c_{mn}(m, n = 0, 1, 2, \cdots)$, where $c_{00} \neq 0$, we set

$$(7) \qquad C_{mn} = \sum_{i=0, j=0}^{m,n} c_{ij}.$$

For any double series $\sum u_{mn}$, where $s_{mn} = \sum\limits_{i=0, j=0}^{m,n} u_{ij}$, we form

$$(8) \qquad \sigma_{mn} = \frac{S_{mn}}{C_{mn}} = \frac{\sum\limits_{i=0, j=0}^{m,n} c_{m-i,n-j} s_{ij}}{C_{mn}}.$$

If σ_{mn} tends to a limit σ as m and n become infinite, we say that the series $\sum u_{mn}$ is summable $(N; c)$ to the value σ.

2.4. **Regularity of the definition for double series.**   We now make use of Theorem VI of Chapter I to determine the conditions under which the definition of the preceding section yields the appropriate value when applied to any convergent double series whose partial sums remain bounded.   We have for the $\varphi_{mn}(\alpha)$ of Theorem VI (I)

$$(9) \qquad \varphi_{ij}(m, n) = \frac{c_{m-i,n-j}}{C_{mn}} \qquad \begin{pmatrix} 0 \leqq i \leqq m \\ 0 \leqq j \leqq n \end{pmatrix},$$

$$\varphi_{ij}(m, n) = 0 \qquad (m < i \text{ or } n < j).$$

The $E(\alpha)$ corresponds to the range $m, n = 0, 1, 2, \cdots$, and α_0 has coordinates (∞, ∞).

---

[16] Cf. [161], [126], [164], and [162].

It is obvious from the definitions (9) that $(A^*)_2$ and $(C^*)_2$ are satisfied in all cases. Condition $(A_1^*)_2$ is equivalent to

$$(10) \qquad \sum_{i=0,\,j=0}^{m,n} |c_{ij}| < H\,|C_{mn}| \qquad \left(\begin{array}{l}H \text{ a positive constant}\\ m,\,n = 0,\,1,\,2,\,\cdots\end{array}\right).$$

Conditions $(E_1^*)_2$ and $(E_2^*)_2$ take the forms

$$(11) \qquad \lim_{m,n\to\infty} \frac{\sum_{j=0}^{n} |c_{m-i,\,n-j}|}{|C_{mn}|} = 0, \qquad \lim_{m,n\to\infty} \frac{\sum_{i=0}^{m} |c_{m-i,\,n-j}|}{|C_{mn}|} = 0,$$

where $0 \le i \le m$ in the first equation, and $0 \le j \le n$ in the second equation. We thus have the theorem:

THEOREM II. *The necessary and sufficient conditions for the regularity of the definition $(N;c)$ of 2.3 in the case of a double series whose partial sums remain bounded are that (10) and (11) should subsist.*

2.5. **Factorable transformations of double sequences.** A special case of the means considered in 2.3, which is of particular interest, arises when the c_{ij} take the form

$$(12) \qquad c_{ij} = c_i^{(1)} c_j^{(2)} \qquad (i,j = 0,\,1,\,2,\,\cdots).$$

The transformation of the double sequence s_{ij}, defined by (8), then falls in the category which Adams has designated as factorable transformations [6]. It is readily seen that if both the $c_i^{(1)}$ and $c_j^{(2)}$ satisfy the necessary and sufficient conditions, (4) and (5), of 2.2, the c_{ij} defined by (12) will satisfy the necessary and sufficient conditions, (10) and (11), of 2.4.

2.6. **Multiple series.** Given an n-tuply infinite set of complex constants $c_{[i]}(i_1,\,i_2,\,\cdots,\,i_n = 0,\,1,\,2,\,\cdots)$, where $c_{[0]} \ne 0$, we set

$$(13) \qquad C_{[m]} = \sum_{i_1=0}^{m_1} \cdots \sum_{i_n=0}^{m_n} c_{[i]}.$$

For any multiple series $\sum u_{[i]}$, where

$$(14) \qquad s_{[m]} = \sum_{i_1=0}^{m_1} \cdots \sum_{i_n=0}^{m_n} u_{[i]},$$

we set

$$(15) \qquad \sigma_{[m]} = \frac{S_{[m]}}{C_{[m]}} = \frac{\sum_{i_1=0}^{m_1} \cdots \sum_{i_n=0}^{m_n} c_{[m-i]}\, s_{[i]}}{C_{[m]}}.$$

If $\sigma_{[m]}$ tends to a limit σ as the m's become infinite, we say that the series $\sum u_{[i]}$ is summable $(N;c)$ to the value σ.

2.7. Regularity of the definition for multiple series.   We make use of Theorem IX (I) to determine the conditions for the regularity of the transformation defined in the previous section.   We have for the $\varphi_{[i]}(\alpha)$ of the theorem referred to

(16)
$$\varphi_{[i]}(m_1, \cdots, m_n) = \frac{c_{[m-i]}}{C_{[m]}} \qquad (0 \leqq i_k \leqq m_k;\ k = 1, 2, \cdots, n),$$

$$\varphi_{[i]}(m_1, \cdots, m_n) = 0 \qquad\qquad (m_k < i_k;\ \text{any } k).$$

The $E(\alpha)$ corresponds to the range $(m_k = 0, 1, 2, \cdots;\ k = 1, 2, \cdots, n)$, and α_0 has coordinates $(\infty, \infty, \cdots, \infty)$.

It follows at once from (16) that $(A^*)_n$ and $(C^*)_n$ are satisfied by the $\varphi_{[i]}$ there defined.   Condition $(A_1^*)_n$ is equivalent to

(17)
$$\sum_{i_1=0}^{m_1} \cdots \sum_{i_n=0}^{m_n} |c_{[i]}| < H |C_{[m]}| \qquad \left(\begin{array}{l} H \text{ a }\quad \text{positive constant} \\ m_k = 0, 1, 2, \cdots;\ k = 1, 2, \cdots, n \end{array}\right).$$

Condition $(E_1^*)_n$ becomes

(18)
$$\lim_{m_1\to\infty,\cdots,m_n\to\infty} \frac{\displaystyle\sum_{i_2=0}^{m_2} \cdots \sum_{i_n=0}^{m_n} |c_{[m-i]}|}{|C_{[m]}|} = 0 \qquad (0 \leqq i_1 \leqq m_1),$$

and the other conditions $(E_s^*)_n$ are obtained by choosing the other combinations of $(n - 1)$ summations in the numerator.

We thus have the result:

THEOREM III.   *The necessary and sufficient conditions for the regularity of the definition $(N; c)$ of 2.6 applied to a multiple series whose partial sums remain bounded are that (17) and the various conditions of the type (18) should subsist.*

2.8. Factorable transformations of multiple series.   When the $c_{[i]}$ take the form

(19)
$$c_{[i]} = c_{i_1}^{(1)} c_{i_2}^{(2)} \cdots c_{i_n}^{(n)}$$

we have the case of a factorable transformation.   It is readily seen that if the various $c_{i_r}^{(r)}$ satisfy the necessary and sufficient conditions of 2.2, the $c_{[i]}$ defined by (19) will satisfy the necessary and sufficient conditions of 2.7.

CHAPTER III

CONVERGENCE FACTORS IN SUMMABLE SERIES

3.1. Lemma on transformation of sequences. For any sequence to function transformation of the form

$$(1) \qquad F(\alpha) = s_0 \varphi_0(\alpha) + s_1 \varphi_1(\alpha) + \cdots + s_n \varphi_n(\alpha) + \cdots \qquad E(\alpha),$$

we know from Lemma 1 (I) that a necessary and sufficient condition for the existence of the transformation in the case of all convergent sequences is (A*) of 1.3. If we wish $F(\alpha)$ to approach a limit as $\alpha \to \alpha_0$, a limit point of $E(\alpha)$ not of the set, we see by considering convergent sequences of the form $s_k = 1$, $s_i = 0$ $(i \neq k)$, where k takes on all integral values ≥ 0, and also convergent sequences of the form $s_i = 1$ $(i = 0, 1, 2, \cdots)$, that further necessary conditions are

$$(C_1^*) \qquad\qquad \lim_{\alpha \to \alpha_0} \varphi_n(\alpha) = \gamma_n \qquad\qquad \text{(all } n),$$

$$(C_2^*) \qquad\quad \lim_{\alpha \to \alpha_0} [\varphi_0(\alpha) + \varphi_1(\alpha) + \varphi_2(\alpha) + \cdots] = \gamma.$$

If we represent by $\sum u_n$ the infinite series whose partial sums form the given sequence and define a set of functions, $f_n(\alpha)$, in terms of the $\varphi_n(\alpha)$ by means of (10) (I), we have from (13) (I)

$$(2) \qquad\qquad F(\alpha) = \sum_{n=0}^{\infty} s_n \Delta f_n(\alpha) = \sum_{n=0}^{\infty} u_n f_n(\alpha).$$

From this equation and the argument used in 1.5 in order to establish the necessity of condition (A_1) of Theorem II (I), we see that an additional necessary condition that $F(\alpha)$ approach a limit as $\alpha \to \alpha_0$ is that the $f_n(\alpha)$ satisfy (A_1) and hence that the $\varphi_n(\alpha)$ satisfy the corresponding condition (A_1^*).

For a null-convergent sequence we infer readily from (1) that the conditions we have stated are sufficient for $F(\alpha)$ to approach a limit as $\alpha \to \alpha_0$, and the general case of a sequence $s_n \to s \neq 0$ reduces to this by using the series $(u_0 - s) + u_1 + u_2 + \cdots$. From (A_1^*) and (C_1^*) we obtain

$$(3) \qquad\qquad |\gamma_0| + |\gamma_1| + \cdots + |\gamma_n| \leq K \qquad\qquad \text{(all } n),$$

and hence the series $\sum \gamma_n$ is absolutely convergent.

Let us set

$$\lim_{n \to \infty} s_n = s, \qquad \lim_{\alpha \to \alpha_0} F(\alpha) = S.$$

From (1) we have

$$(4) \quad \begin{aligned} F(\alpha) &= s[\varphi_0(\alpha) + \varphi_1(\alpha) + \varphi_2(\alpha) + \cdots] \\ &\quad + \{(s_0 - s)\varphi_0(\alpha) + (s_1 - s)\varphi_1(\alpha) + (s_2 - s)\varphi_2(\alpha) + \cdots\}. \end{aligned}$$

It follows readily from (C_1^*) and (A_1^*) that the series in the second term on the right hand side of (4) tends to a limit as $\alpha \to \alpha_0$, which limit may be obtained by taking the limit term by term. From (C_2^*) we see that the limit of the first term exists. Passing to the limit, we obtain

$$(5) \quad S = \lim_{\alpha \to \alpha_0} F(\alpha) = s\gamma + (s_0 - s)\gamma_0 + (s_1 - s)\gamma_1 + (s_2 - s)\gamma_2 + \cdots.$$

We have thus proved the following lemma.[17]

LEMMA 1. *The necessary and sufficient conditions that the sequence to function transformation* (1), *corresponding to any convergent sequence, exist in $E(\alpha)$ and that the $F(\alpha)$ defined by it approach a limit as $\alpha \to \alpha_0$, are that the $\varphi_n(\alpha)$ satisfy conditions* (A^*), (A_1^*), (C_1^*), *and* (C_2^*). *These conditions being satisfied, it follows that the series $\sum \gamma_n$ is absolutely convergent, and that equation* (5) *subsists.*

3.2. **A fundamental identity.** Corresponding to a set of C's defined as in 2.1, we set

$$(6) \quad \frac{1}{C_0 + C_1 z + C_2 z^2 + \cdots} \sim a_0 + a_1 z + a_2 z^2 + \cdots,$$

where the sign $\sim$ is used in the sense that if the expression on the left hand of (6) is formally expanded in ascending powers of z, the coefficients of corresponding terms on the two sides will be equal. We have from (2) (II)

$$\sum_{n=0}^{\infty} S_n z^n \sim \sum s_n z^n \sum c_n z^n \sim (\sum u_n z^n)(1 - z)^{-1} \sum c_n z^n \sim \sum u_n z^n \sum C_n z^n.$$

Hence, making use of (6),

$$(7) \quad \sum u_n z^n \sim \frac{1}{\sum C_n z^n} \sum S_n z^n \sim \sum a_n z^n \sum S_n z^n,$$

and therefore

$$(8) \quad u_n = a_0 S_n + a_1 S_{n-1} + \cdots + a_n S_0.$$

Corresponding to a set of functions, $f_0(\alpha), f_1(\alpha), f_2(\alpha), \cdots$, we define

$$(9) \quad L_p f_n(\alpha) = a_0 f_n(\alpha) + a_1 f_{n+1}(\alpha) + \cdots + a_{p-n} f_p(\alpha).$$

We may then obtain from (8) and (9) the identity

$$(10) \quad \sum_{n=0}^{p} u_n f_n(\alpha) = \sum_{n=0}^{p} S_n L_p f_n(\alpha) = \sum_{n=0}^{p} (S_n/C_n) C_n L_p f_n(\alpha).$$

[17] This is a result due to Schur ([145], p. 82), who proved it for sequence to sequence transformations.

3.3. **Convergence factors of type** I.   Given a series $\sum u_n$ that is summable $(N; c)$ in accordance with the definition in 2.1, we seek necessary and sufficient conditions on a set of functions $f_n(\alpha)$, defined over a set $E(\alpha)$, in order that the series $\sum u_n f_n(\alpha)$ may converge in $E(\alpha)$.   We see from (10) that this is equivalent to the convergence in $E(\alpha)$, as $p \to \infty$, of the right hand side of (10).   It then follows that these conditions may be obtained by an application of Lemma 1, with p playing the rôle of α in that lemma and $\alpha_0 = \infty$.   Condition (C_1^*) implies the existence of

$$(11) \qquad \lim_{p \to \infty} L_p f_n(\alpha) = \sum_{i=0}^{\infty} a_i f_{n+i}(\alpha) = L f_n(\alpha) \qquad\qquad E(\alpha).$$

Conditions (A^*) and (A_1^*) are equivalent to

$$(12) \qquad \sum_{n=0}^{p} |C_n L_p f_n(\alpha)| < M(\alpha) \qquad\qquad E(\alpha),$$

$M(\alpha)$ being independent of p.
    We obtain from the definition of the a's in (6)

$$(13) \qquad C_0 L_p f_0(\alpha) + C_1 L_p f_1(\alpha) + \cdots + C_p L_p f_p(\alpha) = f_0(\alpha) \qquad \text{(all } p),$$

and therefore condition (C_2^*), holding without further restriction, does not enter into the discussion.   If in (13) we allow p to become infinite, we obtain

$$(14) \qquad C_0 L f_0(\alpha) + C_1 L f_1(\alpha) + C_2 L f_2(\alpha) + \cdots = f_0(\alpha).$$

We may also infer from Lemma 1 or directly from (11) and (12)

$$(A) \qquad \sum_{n=0}^{\infty} |C_n L f_n(\alpha)| \leqq M(\alpha) < K(\alpha) \qquad\qquad E(\alpha).$$

If we replace the summation on the left hand side of (12) by its last term, we obtain

$$(B) \qquad |C_n f_n(\alpha)| < M(\alpha) \qquad\qquad (E(\alpha); \text{ all } n).$$

We are going to show that if the definition of summability is regular and the a's defined by (6) satisfy a certain supplementary condition, the conditions (A) and (B) imply (11) and (12) and therefore may be used as the necessary and sufficient conditions for convergence factors of type I.
    Making use of (B), condition (4) of 2.2, and the notation introduced in (6) (II), we have

$$(15) \qquad |C_n f_{n+k}(\alpha)| = \left| \frac{C_n}{C_{n+k}} \right| \cdot |C_{n+k} f_{n+k}(\alpha)| < \frac{G_n}{G_{n+k}/H} M(\alpha) = M_1(\alpha) \quad E(\alpha).$$

From (A) and (15) we obtain

$$\sum_{n=0}^{p} | C_n L_p f_n(\alpha) | \leq \sum_{n=0}^{p} | C_n L f_n(\alpha) | + \sum_{n=0}^{p} | C_n (L_p f_n(\alpha) - L f_n(\alpha)) |$$

$$(16) \qquad < K(\alpha) + \sum_{n=0}^{p} | C_n | \cdot \left| \sum_{m=p-n+1}^{\infty} a_m f_{m+n}(\alpha) \right|$$

$$< K(\alpha) + M_1(\alpha) \sum_{n=1}^{\infty} n | a_n |.$$

If now we make the requirement

$$(17) \qquad \sum_{n=1}^{\infty} n | a_n | < \infty,$$

(12) follows from (16). Condition (11) follows from (17), (B), and condition (4) of 2.2.

We thus have the following theorem:

THEOREM I. *The necessary and sufficient conditions that the series $\sum u_n f_n(\alpha)$ shall converge in $E(\alpha)$ whenever the series $\sum u_n$ is summable $(N; c)$ for a regular definition corresponding to which condition (17) holds, are that the functions $f_n(\alpha)$ satisfy (A) and (B).*

3.4. Convergence factors of type II. We seek next the necessary and sufficient conditions that the series $\sum u_n f_n(\alpha)$ should approach the value to which the series $\sum u_n$ is summable $(N; c)$ as $\alpha \to \alpha_0$, a limit point of $E(\alpha)$, not of the set. If the convergence factors $f_n(\alpha)$ satisfy (A) and (B) of Theorem I, we have from (10), (11), (14), and equation (5) of Lemma 1, using the notations of 2.1,

$$(18) \quad \sum_{n=0}^{\infty} u_n f_n(\alpha) = \sigma f_0(\alpha) + \sum_{n=0}^{\infty} (\sigma_n - \sigma) C_n L f_n(\alpha) = \sum_{n=0}^{\infty} \sigma_n C_n L f_n(\alpha).$$

If we apply Theorem III (I) to the sequence to function transformation defined by the right hand side of (18), we see that the necessary and sufficient conditions, in addition to (A) and (B), that the right hand side of (18) should approach σ as $\alpha \to \alpha_0$, are

$$(A_1) \qquad \sum_{n=0}^{\infty} | C_n L f_n(\alpha) | < K \qquad\qquad E'(\alpha),$$

where $E'(\alpha)$ is a subset of $E(\alpha)$, having α_0 as a limit point, and K is a positive constant,

$$(C_1) \qquad \lim_{\alpha \to \alpha_0} f_0(\alpha) = 1,$$

$$(C_2) \qquad \lim_{\alpha \to \alpha_0} L f_n(\alpha) = 0 \qquad\qquad (\text{all } n).$$

Thus we have the theorem:

THEOREM II. *The necessary and sufficient conditions that the series $\sum u_n f_n(\alpha)$ shall converge in $E(\alpha)$ whenever the series $\sum u_n$ is summable $(N; c)$ for a regular definition corresponding to which (17) holds, and that the first series shall approach* *the value to which the second series is summable as $\alpha \to \alpha_0$, are that the convergence factors $f_n(\alpha)$ satisfy* (A), (A$_1$), (B), (C$_1$), *and* (C$_2$).

3.5. Convergence factor theorems for Cesàro means of integral orders. If we set

$$(19) \qquad c_0 = 1, \quad c_n = c_n^{(r)} = \frac{r(r+1)\cdots(r+n-1)}{n!} \qquad (n \geqq 1),$$

whence

$$(20) \qquad C_0 = 1, \qquad C_n = \frac{(r+1)(r+2)\cdots(r+n)}{n!} \qquad (n \geqq 1),$$

we have from (6) for a positive integral value of r

$$(21) \qquad\qquad a_0 + a_1 z + a_2 z^2 + \cdots = (1-z)^{r+1}.$$

Hence the a's satisfy (17), and

$$(22) \qquad\qquad Lf_n(\alpha) = \Delta^{r+1} f_n(\alpha).$$

Since, from (20), we have $C_n = O(n^r)$, Theorem I yields the following result:

THEOREM III. *The necessary and sufficient conditions that the series $\sum u_n f_n(\alpha)$ shall converge in $E(\alpha)$ whenever the series $\sum u_n$ is summable (Cr), r being a positive integer, are that the functions $f_n(\alpha)$ satisfy*

$$(A) \qquad\qquad \sum_{n=0}^{\infty} n^r \left| \Delta^{r+1} f_n(\alpha) \right| < K(\alpha) \qquad\qquad E(\alpha),$$

$$(B) \qquad\qquad n^r \left| f_n(\alpha) \right| < M(\alpha) \qquad\qquad (E(\alpha), \text{ all } n)$$

$K(\alpha)$ *and* $M(\alpha)$ *being positive functions of* α.

This theorem was obtained by Kojima[18] in 1917.

In the special case we are considering, the right hand side of (22) consists of a finite number of terms, and it is readily seen that condition (C$_1$) and (C$_2$) of Theorem II will hold in case

$$\lim_{\alpha \to \alpha_0} f_n(\alpha) = 1 \qquad\qquad (\text{all } n).$$

Hence we obtain from Theorem II the result:

THEOREM IV. *The necessary and sufficient conditions that the series $\sum u_n f_n(\alpha)$ converge in $E(\alpha)$, whenever $\sum u_n$ is summable (Cr), r being a positive integer, and approach the value to which the latter series is summable as α approaches α_0, are that the convergence factors $f_n(\alpha)$ satisfy conditions* (A) *and* (B) *of Theorem* III *and*

$$(A_1) \qquad\qquad \sum_{n=0}^{\infty} n^r \left| \Delta^{r+1} f_n(\alpha) \right| < K \qquad\qquad E'(\alpha),$$

$$(C) \qquad\qquad \lim_{\alpha \to \alpha_0} f_n(\alpha) = 1, \qquad\qquad (n = 0, 1, 2, \cdots),$$

[18] Cf. [61], Theorem IX.

where $E'(\alpha)$ is some subset of $E(\alpha)$ having α_0 as a limit point and K is a positive constant.

This theorem was obtained by W. A. Hurwitz[19] in 1922.

3.6. **Convergence factors for series summable by Cesàro means of complex orders.**   Theorems I and II also include as special cases criteria for convergence factors in the case of series summable (Cr), where r is any complex constant whose real component exceeds zero.   Equations (19), (20), (21), and (22) subsist in this case, r having the given complex value.   The $\Delta^{r+1}f_n(\alpha)$ in (22) is of course an infinite series in the present instance; the coefficients of its terms satisfy condition (17).   We have then from Theorem I for convergence factors of type I the following result:

THEOREM V.   *If the series $\sum u_n$ is summable (Cr), for any complex r whose real component ρ exceeds zero, the necessary and sufficient conditions for the convergence of $\sum u_n f_n(\alpha)$ in $E(\alpha)$ are that the convergence factors $f_n(\alpha)$ satisfy*

(A)
$$\sum_{n=1}^{\infty} n^{\rho} \, | \, \Delta^{r+1} f_n(\alpha) \, | \, < K(\alpha) \qquad\qquad E(\alpha),$$

(B)
$$n^{\rho} \, | \, f_n(\alpha) \, | \, < M(\alpha) \quad (E(\alpha); n = 1, 2, 3, \cdots),$$

where $K(\alpha)$ and $M(\alpha)$ are positive functions of α.

For the case where r is real but non-integral, Theorem V includes as a special case a sufficient condition for convergence factors of type I, due to Chapman.[20]

By specializing Theorem II to the type of series considered in Theorem V, we obtain the result:

THEOREM VI.   *The necessary and sufficient conditions that the series $\sum u_n f_n(\alpha)$ of Theorem V shall converge in $E(\alpha)$ and approach the value to which $\sum u_n$ is summable (Cr) as $\alpha \to \alpha_0$, are that the convergence factors $f_n(\alpha)$ satisfy (A) and (B) and the following further conditions:*

(A_1)
$$\sum_{n=1}^{\infty} n^{\rho} \, | \, \Delta^{r+1} f_n(\alpha) \, | \, < K \qquad\qquad E'(\alpha),$$

(C_1)
$$\lim_{\alpha \to \alpha_0} f_0(\alpha) = 1,$$

(C_2)
$$\lim_{\alpha \to \alpha_0} \Delta^{r+1} f_n(\alpha) = 0 \qquad (n = 0, 1, 2, \cdots),$$

where K is a positive constant and $E'(\alpha)$ is a subset of $E(\alpha)$, having α_0 as a limit point.

Hurwitz has obtained necessary and sufficient conditions for this case [79]. As his conditions have not been explicitly stated, it is not feasible to compare his results with ours.   Sufficient conditions due to Chapman (loc. cit., §16, Theorem B) may be obtained as a special case of Theorem VI.

---

[19] Cf. [79] and [125], §2.

[20] Cf. [31], §14, Theorem A.

CHAPTER IV

CONVERGENCE FACTORS IN SUMMABLE DOUBLE SERIES

4.1. Lemma on transformation of sequences. For any sequence to function transformation of the form

$$(1) \qquad F(\alpha) = \sum_{m=0,n=0}^{\infty,\infty} s_{mn}\varphi_{mn}(\alpha) \qquad\qquad E(\alpha),$$

we know from Lemma 2 (I) that a necessary and sufficient condition for the existence of the transformation in the case of all convergent bounded sequences is $(A^*)_2$ of 1.9. If we wish $F(\alpha)$ to approach a limit as $\alpha \to \alpha_0$, a limit point of $E(\alpha)$ not of the set, we see by considering convergent sequences of the form $s_{ij} = 1, s_{mn} = 0$ $(m \neq i$ or $n \neq j)$, where i and j each take on all integral values $\geqq 0$, and also convergent sequences of the form $s_{ij} = 1$ $(i, j = 0, 1, 2, \cdots)$, that additional necessary conditions are

$$(C_1^*)_2 \qquad\qquad \lim_{\alpha\to\alpha_0} \varphi_{mn}(\alpha) = \gamma_{mn} \qquad\qquad (\text{all } m, n),$$

$$(C_2^*)_2 \qquad\qquad \lim_{\alpha\to\alpha_0} \sum_{i=0,j=0}^{\infty,\infty} \varphi_{ij}(\alpha) = \gamma.$$

If we represent by $\sum u_{mn}$ the infinite series whose partial sums form the given sequence and define a set of functions, $f_{mn}(\alpha)$, in terms of the $\varphi_{mn}(\alpha)$ by means of (25) (I), we have from (29) (I)

$$(2) \qquad F(\alpha) = \sum_{m=0,n=0}^{\infty,\infty} s_{mn}\Delta_{11}f_{mn}(\alpha) = \sum_{m=0,n=0}^{\infty,\infty} u_{mn}f_{mn}(\alpha).$$

From this equation and the arguments used in 1.11 in order to establish the necessity of $(A_1)_2$ of Theorem V (I), we see that an additional necessary condition that $F(\alpha)$ approach a limit as $\alpha \to \alpha_0$ is that the $f_{mn}(\alpha)$ satisfy $(A_1)_2$ and hence that the $\varphi_{mn}(\alpha)$ satisfy the corresponding condition, $(A_1^*)_2$. From $(A_1^*)_2$ and $(C_1^*)_2$ we obtain

$$(3) \qquad\qquad \sum_{m=0,n=0}^{p,q} |\gamma_{mn}| \leqq K \qquad\qquad (\text{all } p, q),$$

and hence the series $\sum \gamma_{mn}$ is absolutely convergent.

We next show that the following further conditions are necessary:

$$(E_1) \qquad\qquad \lim_{\alpha\to\alpha_0} \sum_{m=0,n=j}^{\lambda,\infty} |\gamma_{mn} - \varphi_{mn}(\alpha)| = 0 \qquad\qquad (\text{all } \lambda, j),$$

$$(E_2) \qquad\qquad \lim_{\alpha\to\alpha_0} \sum_{m=i,n=0}^{\infty,\mu} |\gamma_{mn} - \varphi_{mn}(\alpha)| = 0 \qquad\qquad (\text{all } i, \mu).$$

Since the proofs for (E_1) and (E_2) are analogous, we consider only (E_1).   If this condition does not hold, then there can be found a value of λ, λ_1, and a positive ϵ, such that for each value of j there exists a set of values of α, $\alpha = \alpha_k^{(j)}$ ($k = 1$, $2, 3, \cdots$), tending to α_0 such that

(4) $$\sum_{m=0,n=j}^{\lambda_1,\infty} | \gamma_{mn} - \varphi_{mn}(\alpha) | > \epsilon \qquad\qquad (\text{all } j, \alpha = \alpha_k^{(j)} \ (k = 1, 2, 3, \cdots)).$$

We first select a value of j, j_1, such that

(5) $$\sum_{m=0,n=j}^{\lambda_1,\infty} | \gamma_{mn} | < \frac{\epsilon}{10} \qquad\qquad (j \geqq j_1),$$

which is possible in view of the absolute convergence of $\sum \gamma_{mn}$.   We then choose one of the values of $\alpha_k^{(j)}$, corresponding to j_1, which we designate as α_1.   Since condition $(A^*)_2$ is satisfied, we can find a $q_1 > j_1$, such that

(6) $$\sum_{m=0,n=j}^{\lambda_1,\infty} | \varphi_{mn}(\alpha_1) | < \frac{\epsilon}{10} \qquad\qquad (j > q_1).$$

We are going to make a choice of the s_{mn} which will lead to a contradiction by use of the above consequences of our supposition that (E_1) is not satisfied.   We first set

(7) $$s_{mn} = 0 \qquad\qquad (0 \leqq m, 0 \leqq n < j_1 \, ; \lambda_1 < m, j_1 \leqq n).$$

The s_{mn} not defined by (7) will be chosen in steps, but all choices will be made in such a manner that

(8) $$| s_{mn} | \leqq 1 \qquad\qquad (0 \leqq m \leqq \lambda_1 , j_1 \leqq n).$$

We begin by setting

(9) $$s_{mn} = \operatorname{sgn} [\varphi_{mn}(\alpha_1) - \gamma_{mn}] \qquad\qquad (0 \leqq m \leqq \lambda_1 , j_1 \leqq n \leqq q_1).$$

In view of (1), (7), and (9) we have

(10) $$F(\alpha_1) = \sum_{m=0,n=j_1}^{\lambda_1,q_1} | \varphi_{mn}(\alpha_1) - \gamma_{mn} | + \sum_{m=0,n=j_1}^{\lambda_1,q_1} s_{mn} \gamma_{mn} + \sum_{m=0,n=q_1+1}^{\lambda_1,\infty} s_{mn} \varphi_{mn}(\alpha_1).$$

From (10), (4), (5), (6), and (8) we have

(11) $$F(\alpha_1) > \tfrac{6}{10}\epsilon > \tfrac{1}{2}\epsilon.$$

We next choose a value of j, $j_2 > q_1$, and among the $\alpha_k^{(j)}$ corresponding to j_2 we select α_2 nearer to α_0 than α_1, and such that

(12) $$\sum_{m=0,n=j_1}^{\lambda_1,j_2-1} | \varphi_{mn}(\alpha_2) - \gamma_{mn} | < \frac{\epsilon}{10},$$

which we can do in view of $(C_1^*)_2$.   We then select a $q_2 > j_2$ and such that

(13) $$\sum_{m=0,n=j}^{\lambda_1,\infty} | \varphi_{mn}(\alpha_2) | < \frac{\epsilon}{10} \qquad\qquad (j > q_2).$$

Then we set $s_{mn} = 1$ for $(0 \leqq m \leqq \lambda_1, q_1 < n < j_2)$, and

$$(14) \qquad\qquad s_{mn} = -\operatorname{sgn}[\varphi_{mn}(\alpha_2) - \gamma_{mn}] \qquad\qquad (0 \leqq m \leqq \lambda_1, j_2 \leqq n \leqq q_2).$$

If the s_{mn} are chosen in accordance with (7), (8), (9), and (14), we infer from the inequalities (4), (5), (12), and (13) that

$$(15) \qquad\qquad\qquad\qquad F(\alpha_2) < -\tfrac{1}{2}\epsilon.$$

Continuing the choices of the s_{mn} not primarily designated, in the manner above indicated, we define a bounded double sequence converging to zero, for which $F(\alpha)$ oscillates between values $> \tfrac{1}{2}\epsilon$ and $< -\tfrac{1}{2}\epsilon$, as α tends to α_0. Thus we have a contradiction, and the necessity of (E_1) is established. As indicated before, the proof of the necessity of (E_2) is analogous.

For any bounded, convergent sequence, s_{mn}, we infer readily from (1) that if the $\varphi_{mn}(\alpha)$ satisfy conditions $(A^*)_2$, $(A_1^*)_2$, $(C_1^*)_2$, $(C_2^*)_2$, (E_1), and (E_2), the $F(\alpha)$ defined by (1) will tend to the value of the absolutely convergent series

$$(16) \qquad\qquad\qquad\qquad \sum_{m=0, n=0}^{\infty, \infty} \gamma_{mn} s_{mn},$$

and the partial sums of the series in (1) will remain bounded for each α in $E(\alpha)$. If we designate the limit of s_{mn} by s and the value of the series in (16) by S, we have

$$(17) \qquad\qquad S = \lim_{\alpha \to \alpha_0} F(\alpha) = s\gamma + \sum_{m=0, n=0}^{\infty, \infty} (s_{mn} - s)\gamma_{mn}.$$

We thus have the result:

LEMMA 1. *The necessary and sufficient conditions that the sequence to function transformation* (1), *corresponding to any bounded, convergent double sequence, exi.. in $E(\alpha)$, that the $F(\alpha)$ defined by it approach a limit as $\alpha \to \alpha_0$, and that the partial sums of the series on the right hand side of* (1) *remain bounded for each α in $E(\alpha)$, are that the $\varphi_{mn}(\alpha)$ satisfy $(A^*)_2$, $(A_1^*)_2$, $(C_1^*)_2$, $(C_2^*)_2$, (E_1), and (E_2). These conditions being satisfied, it follows that the series $\sum \gamma_{mn}$ is absolutely convergent and that equation* (17) *subsists.*

4.2. **A fundamental identity.** Corresponding to a set of C_{ij}'s defined as in 2.3 we put

$$(18) \qquad\qquad 1 \bigg/ \sum_{i=0, j=0}^{\infty, \infty} C_{ij} x^i y^j \sim \sum_{i=0, j=0}^{\infty, \infty} a_{ij} x^i y^j,$$

where the sign $\sim$ is used in the sense that if the expression on the left hand side of (18) is formally expanded in a double power series in x and y, the coefficients of corresponding terms on the two sides will be equal.

We have from (8) (II)

$$\sum_{i=0,\,j=0}^{\infty,\infty} S_{ij}x^i y^j \sim \sum s_{ij}x^i y^j \sum c_{ij}x^i y^j$$

$$\sim \left(\sum u_{ij}x^i y^j\right)(1-x)^{-1}(1-y)^{-1}\sum c_{ij}x^i y^j$$

$$\sim \sum u_{ij}x^i y^j \sum C_{ij}x^i y^j.$$

Hence, from (18),

(19) $$\sum u_{ij}x^i y^j \sim \sum a_{ij}x^i y^j \sum S_{ij}x^i y^j,$$

and therefore

(20) $$u_{mn} = \sum_{i=0,\,j=0}^{m,n} a_{ij}S_{m-i,n-j}.$$

Corresponding to a set of functions, $f_{ij}(\alpha)$, we define

(21) $$L_{pq}f_{mn}(\alpha) = \sum_{i=0,\,j=0}^{p-m,\,q-n} a_{ij}f_{m+i,\,n+j}(\alpha) \qquad (p \geqq m,\ q \geqq n).$$

We may then obtain from (20) and (21) the identity

(22) $$\sum_{m=0,\,n=0}^{p,q} u_{mn}f_{mn}(\alpha) = \sum_{m=0,\,n=0}^{p,q} S_{mn}L_{pq}f_{mn}(\alpha) = \sum_{m=0,\,n=0}^{p,q} (S_{mn}/C_{mn})C_{mn}L_{pq}f_{mn}(\alpha).$$

4.3. Convergence factors of type I. Given a double series $\sum u_{mn}$ which is summable $(N;c)$ in accordance with the definition in 2.3, and which satisfies

(23) $$|S_{mn}/C_{mn}| < M \qquad (M \text{ a constant; all } m, n),$$

we seek necessary and sufficient conditions on a set of functions, $f_{mn}(\alpha)$, defined over a set $E(\alpha)$, in order that the series $\sum u_{mn}f_{mn}(\alpha)$ may converge in $E(\alpha)$. We see from (22) that this is equivalent to the convergence in $E(\alpha)$, as p and $q \to \infty$, of the right hand side of (22). We may therefore obtain a set of conditions by an application of Lemma 1, with (p, q) playing the rôle of α, and $\alpha_0 = (\infty, \infty)$. Condition $(C_1^*)_2$ implies the existence of

(24) $$\lim_{p,q\to\infty} L_{pq}f_{mn}(\alpha) = \sum_{i=0,\,j=0}^{\infty,\infty} a_{ij}f_{m+i,\,n+j}(\alpha) = Lf_{mn}(\alpha) \qquad E(\alpha).$$

We have from the definition of the a's in (18)

(25) $$\sum_{i=0,\,j=0}^{p,q} C_{ij}L_{pq}f_{ij}(\alpha) = f_{00}(\alpha) \qquad (\text{all } p, q),$$

and therefore condition $(C_2^*)_2$, holding without further restriction, does not enter into the discussion. Conditions $(A^*)_2$ and $(A_1^*)_2$ are equivalent to

(26) $$\sum_{m=0,\,n=0}^{p,q} |C_{mn}L_{pq}f_{mn}(\alpha)| < M(\alpha),$$

$M(\alpha)$ being independent of p and q. Conditions (E_1) and (E_2) take the form

$$(27) \quad \lim_{p,q\to\infty} \sum_{m=0}^{\lambda} \left\{ \sum_{n=r}^{q} C_{mn}[Lf_{mn}(\alpha) - L_{pq}f_{mn}(\alpha)] + \sum_{n=q+1}^{\infty} C_{mn}Lf_{mn}(\alpha) \right\} = 0$$

$$(E(\alpha); \text{ all } \lambda, r),$$

$$(28) \quad \lim_{p,q\to\infty} \sum_{n=0}^{\mu} \left\{ \sum_{m=k}^{p} C_{mn}[Lf_{mn}(\alpha) - L_{pq}f_{mn}(\alpha)] + \sum_{m=p+1}^{\infty} C_{mn}Lf_{mn}(\alpha) \right\} = 0$$

$$(E(\alpha); \text{ all } k, \mu).$$

We thus see that (24), (26), (27), and (28) constitute a set of necessary and sufficient conditions for convergence factors of type I. They can be replaced, however, by another set of conditions, simpler in form and more easily verified. We proceed to obtain this new set of conditions.

We may infer from Lemma 1, or directly from (24) and (26),

$$(A)_2 \qquad \sum_{m=0,\,n=0}^{\infty,\infty} |C_{mn}Lf_{mn}(\alpha)| \leqq M(\alpha) < K(\alpha) \qquad E(\alpha),$$

$K(\alpha)$ being a positive function of α, defined in $E(\alpha)$. If we replace the summation on the left hand side of (26) by the term for which $m = p$, $n = q$, we obtain

$$(B)_2 \qquad |C_{mn}f_{mn}(\alpha)| < M(\alpha) \qquad (E(\alpha); \text{ all } m, n).$$

We next introduce some further notations

$$(29) \qquad L_j^{(1)}f_{mn}(\alpha) = \sum_{i=0}^{\infty} a_{ij}f_{m+i,n}(\alpha) \qquad (\text{all } j, m, n),$$

$$(30) \qquad L_i^{(2)}f_{mn}(\alpha) = \sum_{j=0}^{\infty} a_{ij}f_{m,n+j}(\alpha) \qquad (\text{all } i, m, n).$$

We then make the following additional requirements:

$$(D_1^{(1)}) \qquad \lim_{n\to\infty} C_{mn}L_j^{(1)}f_{m,n+j}(\alpha) = 0 \qquad (E(\alpha); \text{ all } m, j);$$

there exists a set of positive constants $A_j^{(1)}$, such that

$$(31) \qquad \sum_{j=0}^{\infty} jA_j^{(1)} < A_1 < \infty,$$

and

$$(D_1^{(2)}) \qquad \sum_{m=0}^{\infty} |C_{mn}L_j^{(1)}f_{m,n+j}(\alpha)| \leqq A_j^{(1)}K_1(\alpha) \qquad (E(\alpha); \text{ all } n, j),$$

where $K_1(\alpha)$ is a positive function of α, defined in $E(\alpha)$;

$$(D_2^{(1)}) \qquad \lim_{m\to\infty} C_{mn}L_i^{(2)}f_{m+i,n}(\alpha) = 0 \qquad (E(\alpha); \text{ all } n, i);$$

there exists a set of positive constants $A_i^{(2)}$, such that

$$(32) \qquad \sum_{i=0}^{\infty} i A_i^{(2)} < A_2 < \infty$$

and

$$(D_2^{(2)}) \qquad \sum_{n=0}^{\infty} | C_{mn} L_i^{(2)} f_{m+i,n}(\alpha) | \leq A_i^{(2)} K_2(\alpha) \qquad (E(\alpha); \text{ all } m, i),$$

where $K_2(\alpha)$ is a positive function of α, defined in $E(\alpha)$.

We are going to show first that if the definition of summability is regular and the a's defined by (18) satisfy the supplementary condition

$$(33) \qquad \sum_{m=0,\,n=0}^{\infty,\infty} (m+1)(n+1) | a_{mn} | < A < \infty,$$

conditions $(A)_2$, $(B)_2$, $(D_1^{(1)})$, $(D_1^{(2)})$, $(D_2^{(1)})$, and $(D_2^{(2)})$ imply (24), (26), (27), and (28), and may therefore be used as sufficient conditions for convergence factors of type I under the restrictions stated.

The convergence of the double series in (24) follows from $(B)_2$ and (33), if we take into account (10) of 2.4 and the basic assumption $c_{00} \neq 0$. We also make use of (10) of 2.4 to derive from $(B)_2$ a more general inequality than $(B)_2$ itself.

Let us set

$$(34) \qquad G_{mn} = \sum_{i=0,\,j=0}^{m,n} | c_{ij} |.$$

Then we have

$$(35) \qquad | C_{mn} f_{m+i,n+j}(\alpha) | = \left| \frac{C_{mn}}{C_{m+i,n+j}} \right| \cdot | C_{m+i,n+j} f_{m+i,n+j}(\alpha) | < \frac{G_{mn}}{G_{m+i,n+j}/H} M(\alpha)$$

$$\leq H \cdot M(\alpha) = M_1(\alpha) \qquad (E(\alpha); \text{ all } m, n, i, j),$$

where $M_1(\alpha)$ is a positive function of α, defined in $E(\alpha)$.

If we can show that for each α in $E(\alpha)$

$$(36) \qquad \sum_{m=0,\,n=0}^{p,q} C_{mn} [L f_{mn}(\alpha) - L_{pq} f_{mn}(\alpha)]$$

remains bounded for all p, q, it will follow that (26) will hold whenever $(A)_2$ holds. We may write

$$(37) \qquad L f_{mn}(\alpha) - L_{pq} f_{mn}(\alpha) = \left[\sum_{i=0,\,j=q-n+1}^{p-m,\infty} + \sum_{i=p-m+1,\,j=0}^{\infty,q-n} \right. $$
$$\left. + \sum_{i=p-m+1,\,j=q-n+1}^{\infty,\infty} \right] a_{ij} f_{m+i,\,n+j}(\alpha).$$

It follows readily from (35) and (33) that the portion of the expression in (36) corresponding to the third summation on the right hand side of (37) remains finite for all choices of p and q, α having any fixed value in $E(\alpha)$. A similar conclusion with regard to the portion corresponding to the first summation may be drawn from (23), $(D_1^{(2)})$, (31), (35), and (33). For the discussion of the portion corresponding to the second summation we replace $(D_1^{(2)})$ and (31) by $(D_2^{(2)})$ and (32).

In view of $(A)_2$ the derivation of (27) and (28) reduces to that of the following relations

$$(38) \qquad \lim_{p,q\to\infty} \sum_{m=0,\ n=r}^{\lambda,q} C_{mn}[Lf_{mn}(\alpha) - L_{pq}f_{mn}(\alpha)] = 0 \qquad (E(\alpha);\ \text{all } \lambda, r),$$

$$(39) \qquad \lim_{p,q\to\infty} \sum_{m=k,\ n=0}^{p,\mu} C_{mn}[Lf_{mn}(\alpha) - L_{pq}f_{mn}(\alpha)] = 0 \qquad (E(\alpha);\ \text{all } k, \mu).$$

Since the proof in the case of (39) is entirely equivalent to that in the case of (38), we shall give the details of the latter proof only. It follows from (33) that the portion of the summation in (38) corresponding to the last summation in (37) will for a fixed λ, r, and α tend to zero as $p \to \infty$, uniformly for all q. The discussion of the portion corresponding to the second summation in (37) is analogous to that corresponding to the first summation, so we shall confine ourselves to the latter case. If we make use of the notation (29), the portion in question may be written in the form

$$(40) \qquad \sum_{m=0,\ n=r}^{\lambda,q} C_{mn}\left[\sum_{j=q-n+1}^{\infty} L_j^{(1)} f_{m,n+j}(\alpha) - \sum_{i=p-m+1,\ j=q-n+1}^{\infty,\infty} a_{mn}f_{m+i,n+j}(\alpha) \right].$$

That the portion of (40) corresponding to the second summation in brackets tends to zero uniformly in q as $p \to \infty$, for a fixed λ, r, and α, follows from (33). We consider then the portion corresponding to the first summation in brackets.

It follows from $(D_1^{(2)})$ and (31) that, corresponding to a given positive ϵ, we can choose a value of n, n_1, such that for $q \geq n_1 + r$ we have for a fixed α

$$(41) \qquad \left| \sum_{m=0,\ n=q-n_1+1}^{\lambda,q} C_{mn} \sum_{j=n_1+1}^{\infty} L_j^{(1)} f_{m,n+j}(\alpha) \right|$$

$$< K_1(\alpha)n_1 \sum_{j=n_1+1}^{\infty} A_j^{(1)} < K_1(\alpha) \sum_{j=n_1}^{\infty} jA_j^{(1)} < \tfrac{1}{3}\epsilon.$$

Then in view of $(D_1^{(1)})$, we can choose $q_1 \geq n_1 + r$ and such that

$$(42) \qquad \left| \sum_{m=0,\ n=q-n_1+1}^{\lambda,q} C_{mn} \sum_{j=q-n+1}^{n_1} L_j^{(1)} f_{m,n+j}(\alpha) \right| < \tfrac{1}{3}\epsilon \qquad (q \geq q_1)$$

for a fixed λ and α. We also have for $q \geq n_1 + r$

$$(43) \qquad \left| \sum_{m=0,\ n=r}^{\lambda,q-n_1+1} C_{mn} \sum_{j=q-n+1}^{\infty} L_j^{(1)} f_{m,n+j}(\alpha) \right| < K_1(\alpha) \sum_{n=r}^{q-n_1+1} \sum_{j=q-n+1}^{\infty} A_j^{(1)}$$

$$< K_1(\alpha) \sum_{j=n_1}^{\infty} jA_j^{(1)} < \tfrac{1}{3}\epsilon.$$

Combining (41), (42), and (43), we see that the portion of (40) corresponding to the first summation in brackets can be made less in absolute value than a given positive ϵ by choosing q sufficiently large.

We have thus completed the proof that (24), (26), (27), and (28) follow from $(A)_2$, $(B)_2$, $(D_1^{(1)})$, $(D_1^{(2)})$, $(D_2^{(1)})$, and $(D_2^{(2)})$ in the case of a regular definition corresponding to which (33) holds. It therefore follows that the latter group of conditions are sufficient conditions for convergence factors of type I in the case considered. We turn to the discussion of their necessity.

4.4. Necessity of the conditions. We are seeking conditions that will at the same time be necessary and sufficient for *all* definitions of the type considered, and therefore we are at liberty to introduce special forms of such definitions in connection with the necessity proofs when need arises. This remark should be kept in mind when reading the subsequent proof of the necessity of $(D_1^{(2)})$.

Since $(A)_2$ is a consequence of the necessary conditions (24) and (26), and $(B)_2$ is implied by the necessary condition (26), the necessity of $(A)_2$ and $(B)_2$ is established.

We consider next condition $(D_1^{(1)})$, noting that the discussion of $(D_2^{(1)})$ is entirely analogous. In view of (22) we have

$$(44) \qquad \sum_{m=0,\,n=0}^{p,q} u_{mn} f_{mn}(\alpha) = \sum_{m=0,\,n=0}^{p,q} S_{mn} \sum_{j=0}^{q-n} L_j^{(1)} f_{m,n+j}(\alpha)$$
$$- \sum_{m=0,\,n=0}^{p,q} S_{mn} \sum_{i=p-m+1,\,j=0}^{\infty,q-n} a_{ij} f_{m+i,n+j}(\alpha).$$

If $(D_1^{(1)})$ does not hold for some particular value of α, we can find an $\epsilon > 0$, an m_1 and a λ_1 such that

$$(45) \qquad \left| C_{m_1 n} \sum_{j=0}^{\lambda_1} L_j^{(1)} f_{m_1,n+j}(\alpha) \right| > \epsilon$$

for an infinite number of choices of $n, n_1, n_2, n_3, \cdots$. We then choose $S_{m_1 n_1} = |C_{m_1 n_1}|$, and take $q_1 = n_1 + \lambda_1$, $p_1 > m_1$, and sufficiently large to make

$$\left| C_{m_1 n_1} \sum_{i=p_1-m_1+1,\,j=0}^{\infty,q_1-n_1} a_{ij} f_{m_1+i,n_1+j}(\alpha) \right| < \tfrac{1}{2}\epsilon,$$

which is possible, in view of $(B)_2$, already proved necessary, and (33). We further choose $S_{mn} = 0$ for all other combinations of (m, n) which satisfy the inequalities $0 \leq m \leq p$, $0 \leq n \leq q$.

We next take $q_2 = n_2 + \lambda_1$ and $p_2 > p_1$ and sufficiently large to make

$$\left| C_{m_1 n_1} \sum_{i=p_2-m_1+1,\,j=0}^{\infty,q_2-n_1} a_{ij} f_{m_1+i,n_1+j}(\alpha) \right| + \left| C_{m_1 n_1} \sum_{i=p_2-m_1+1,\,j=0}^{\infty,q_2-n_2} a_{ij} f_{m_1+i,n_2+j}(\alpha) \right| < \tfrac{1}{2}\epsilon.$$

Let us set

$$P_1 = S_{m_1 n_1} \sum_{j=0}^{\lambda_1} L_j^{(1)} f_{m_1,n_1+j}(\alpha), \qquad P_2 = S_{m_1 n_1} \sum_{j=0}^{q_2-n_1} L_j^{(1)} f_{m_1,n_1+j}(\alpha).$$

If $P_2 \neq P_1$, we set

$$S_{m_1 n_2} = \left[|C_{m_1 n_2}| \operatorname{sgn} \sum_{j=0}^{\lambda_1} L_j^{(1)} f_{m_1, n_1+j}(\alpha) \right] \frac{P_2 - P_1}{|P_2 - P_1|}.$$

If $P_2 = P_1$, we make the same choice with the omission of the indeterminate factor $(P_2 - P_1)/|P_2 - P_1|$. The other S's, whose indices lie in the range $(0 \leq p \leq p_2, \ 0 \leq q \leq q_2)$ and which have not been previously defined, are chosen equal to zero.

If we continue our choices of q and p and the S's in accordance with the above procedure, we see that for each succeeding choice the first term on the right hand side of (44) changes by a quantity which exceeds ϵ in absolute value, whereas the second term remains constantly less than $\frac{1}{2}\epsilon$ in absolute value. Thus the right hand side of (44) does not approach a limit as p and q become infinite in this manner. But the series defined by our choice of S's is summable $(N; c)$ to zero, and satisfies (23). Hence the left hand side of (44) should approach a limit as p and q become infinite in any manner. The contradiction thus established proves the necessity of $(D_1^{(1)})$.

We take up next condition $(D_1^{(2)})$, noting that the proof for $(D_2^{(2)})$ is analogous. To establish the necessity of $(D_1^{(2)})$ we consider the case where the a_{mn} of (18) take the form $a_m^{(2)} a_n^{(1)}$. Then if we set

$$(46) \qquad L_1 f_{mn}(\alpha) = \sum_{i=0}^{\infty} a_i f_{m+i, n}(\alpha),$$

we have from (29)

$$L_j^{(1)} f_{mn}(\alpha) = a_j^{(1)} L_1 f_{mn}(\alpha),$$

and if we let $A_j^{(1)} = |a_j^{(1)}|$, it follows from (33) that the $A_j^{(1)}$ thus defined satisfy (31). In order to show then that $(D_1^{(2)})$ is necessary, we need to show that

$$(47) \qquad \sum_{m=0}^{\infty} |C_{mn} L_1 f_{m, n+j}(\alpha)| < K_1(\alpha) \qquad\qquad (E(\alpha); \text{ all } n)$$

must hold for every j for which $a_j^{(1)}$ is different from zero. If (47) does not hold for some value of α in $E(\alpha)$, we can find an n_1 and a j_1, where $a_j^{(1)} \neq 0$, and such that

$$(48) \qquad \sum_{m=0}^{p} |C_{mn_1} L_1 f_{m, n_1+j_1}(\alpha)|$$

increases indefinitely as $p \to \infty$ over a set of values $p_1, p_2, \cdots$.

If we set

$$(49) \qquad \sigma_{pq}(\alpha) = \sum_{m=0, \ n=0}^{p, q} u_{mn} f_{mn}(\alpha),$$

we have from (44), taking $q_1 = n_1 + j_1$, and setting $S_{mn} = 0$, whenever $n \neq n_1$,

$$\sigma_{pq_1}(\alpha) - \sigma_{p,q_1-1}(\alpha) = a_{j_1}^{(1)} \sum_{m=0}^{p} S_{mn_1} L_1 f_{m,n_1+j_1}(\alpha)$$

(50)

$$- a_{j_1}^{(1)} \sum_{m=0}^{p} S_{mn_1} \sum_{i=p-m+1}^{\infty} a_i^{(2)} f_{m+i,n_1+j_1}(\alpha).$$

If now we put

$$S_{mn_1} = |C_{mn_1}| \operatorname{sgn} L_1 f_{m,n_1+j_1}(\alpha) \qquad \text{(all } m\text{)},$$

it follows from (35) and (33) that the second term on the right hand side of (50) remains bounded as p becomes infinite. Since, however, (48) increases indefinitely as $p_k \to \infty$, it follows that the first term on the right hand side does likewise, $a_j^{(1)}$ being different from zero. Hence the left hand side of (50) increases indefinitely as p_k becomes infinite, and therefore the partial sums of the series $\sum u_{mn} f_{mn}(\alpha)$ do not form a bounded sequence. This is a contradiction, and $(D_1^{(2)})$ is thus seen to be necessary.

As pointed out before, the proofs of the necessity of $(D_2^{(1)})$ and $(D_2^{(2)})$ are analogous to those of $(D_1^{(1)})$ and $(D_1^{(2)})$, just given. We may therefore regard the necessity of all four conditions as established.

We have thus proved the following theorem:

THEOREM I. *The necessary and sufficient conditions for all definitions* $(N; c)$ *which are regular and satisfy the supplementary condition* (33) *that the series* $\sum u_{mn} f_{mn}(\alpha)$ *shall converge in* $E(\alpha)$ *and have its partial sums bounded for each* α, *whenever the series* $\sum u_{mn}$ *is summable* $(N; c)$ *and satisfies* (23), *are that the convergence factors* $f_{mn}(\alpha)$ *should satisfy* (A)$_2$, (B)$_2$, $(D_1^{(1)})$, $(D_1^{(2)})$, $(D_2^{(1)})$, *and* $(D_2^{(2)})$.

4.5. **Convergence factors of type II.** We seek next the necessary and sufficient conditions that the series $\sum u_{mn} f_{mn}(\alpha)$ should also approach the value to which the series $\sum u_{mn}$ is summable $(N; c)$ as $\alpha \to \alpha_0$, a limit point of $E(\alpha)$, not of the set. If the convergence factors satisfy the conditions of Theorem I, we have from (22), (24), (25), and (17), using the notations of 2.3,

$$\sum_{m=0, n=0}^{\infty,\infty} u_{mn} f_{mn}(\alpha) = \sigma f_{00}(\alpha) + \sum_{m=0, n=0}^{\infty,\infty} (\sigma_{mn} - \sigma) C_{mn} L f_{mn}(\alpha)$$

(51)

$$= \sum_{m=0, n=0}^{\infty,\infty} \sigma_{mn} C_{mn} L f_{mn}(\alpha) \qquad E(\alpha).$$

If we apply Theorem VI (I) to the sequence to function transformation defined by the right hand side of (51), we see that the necessary and sufficient conditions, in addition to those of Theorem I, that the expression in question should tend to σ as $\alpha \to \alpha_0$ are

(A$_1$)$_2$

$$\sum_{m=0, n=0}^{\infty,\infty} |C_{mn} L f_{mn}(\alpha)| < K \qquad E'(\alpha),$$

where K is a positive constant and $E'(\alpha)$ is a subset of $E(\alpha)$, having α_0 as a limit point,

$(C_1)_2$
$$\lim_{\alpha \to \alpha_0} f_{00}(\alpha) = 1,$$

$(C_2)_2$
$$\lim_{\alpha \to \alpha_0} L f_{mn}(\alpha) = 0 \qquad \text{(all } m, n),$$

(E_1)
$$\lim_{\alpha \to \alpha_0} \sum_{n=0}^{\infty} | C_{mn} L f_{mn}(\alpha) | = 0 \qquad \text{(all } m),$$

(E_2)
$$\lim_{\alpha \to \alpha_0} \sum_{m=0}^{\infty} | C_{mn} L f_{mn}(\alpha) | = 0 \qquad \text{(all } n).$$

We have thus established:

THEOREM II. *The necessary and sufficient conditions for all definitions* $(N; c)$ *which are regular and satisfy the supplementary condition* (33), *that the series* $\sum u_{mn} f_{mn}(\alpha)$ *converge in* $E(\alpha)$ *and have its partial sums bounded for each* α, *whenever* $\sum u_{mn}$ *is summable* $(N; c)$ *and satisfies* (23), *and furthermore approach the value to which the latter series is summable as* $\alpha \to \alpha_0$, *are that the functions* $f_{mn}(\alpha)$ *satisfy conditions* $(A)_2$, $(A_1)_2$, $(B)_2$, $(C_1)_2$, $(C_2)_2$, $(D_1^{(1)})$, $(D_2^{(1)})$, $(D_1^{(2)})$, $(D_2^{(2)})$, (E_1), *and* (E_2).

4.6. **Convergence factor theorems for Cesàro means of integral orders.** If we set

(52)
$$c_{mn} = c_m^{(k)} c_n^{(r)},$$

where $c_n^{(r)}$ and $c_m^{(k)}$ are defined by (19) (III), we have the case of Cesàro summability for double series. Suppose first that k and r are positive integers. We have from (52) and (24)

(53)
$$L f_{mn}(\alpha) = \Delta_{k+1, r+1} f_{mn}(\alpha)$$
$$= \sum_{i=0, j=0}^{k+1, r+1} (-1)^i (-1)^j \binom{k+1}{k+1-i} \binom{r+1}{r+1-j} f_{m+i, n+j}(\alpha).$$

We shall say that a double series which satisfies a condition of the form (23), with the c's defined as in (52), is bounded (C, k, r). We then obtain as a special case of Theorem I the following result:

THEOREM III. *The necessary and sufficient conditions that the series* $\sum u_{mn} f_{mn}(\alpha)$ *shall converge and have its partial sums bounded for each* α *in* $E(\alpha)$ *whenever the series* $\sum u_{mn}$ *is summable and bounded* (C, k, r), k *and* r *being positive integers, are that the functions* $f_{mn}(\alpha)$ *satisfy*

$(A)_2$
$$\sum_{m=0,\,n=0}^{\infty,\infty} m^k n^r \, |\, \Delta_{k+1,r+1} f_{mn}(\alpha)\,| \; < \; K(\alpha) \qquad\qquad E(\alpha),$$

$(B)_2$
$$m^k n^r \,|f_{mn}(\alpha)\,| \; < \; M(\alpha) \qquad (E(\alpha);\text{ all } m,\, n),$$

$(D_1^{(1)})$
$$\lim_{n\to\infty} n^r \Delta_{k+1,0} f_{mn}(\alpha) \; = \; 0 \qquad (E(\alpha);\text{ all } m),$$

$(D_1^{(2)})$
$$n^r \sum_{m=0}^{\infty} m^k \,|\, \Delta_{k+1,0} f_{mn}(\alpha)\,| \; < \; K_1(\alpha) \qquad (E(\alpha);\text{ all } n),$$

$(D_2^{(1)})$
$$\lim_{m\to\infty} m^k \Delta_{0,r+1} f_{mn}(\alpha) \; = \; 0 \qquad (E(\alpha);\text{ all } n),$$

$(D_2^{(2)})$
$$m^k \sum_{n=0}^{\infty} n^r \,|\, \Delta_{0,r+1} f_{mn}(\alpha)\,| \; < \; K_2(\alpha) \qquad (E(\alpha);\text{ all } m),$$

where $K(\alpha)$, $M(\alpha)$, $K_1(\alpha)$, and $K_2(\alpha)$ are positive functions of α, defined in $E(\alpha)$.

It should be noted here that in this special case the infinite series in (31) and (32) reduce to finite sums, so that no question of the convergence of these series arises. Furthermore the rate of increase of C_{mn} with increasing m and n is such that, for a fixed i or j, $|\,C_{m+i,n}/C_{mn}\,|$ and $|\,C_{m,n+j}/C_{mn}\,|$ remain bounded for all choices of m and n. This property of the C_{mn} enables us to simplify the form of statement of conditions of type (D).

The special case of Theorem III where k and r are equal and the set $E(\alpha)$ is in a space of two dimensions has been treated by Moore in [121], where the conditions are given in slightly different form. With regard to conditions (B_1) and (B_2) in Theorem I of the paper in question, which correspond to conditions of type (D) in Theorem III, there is an omission in the statement. In addition to the existence of the indicated limits, it should be required that the expression in (B_1) remain finite for all j and p and the expression in (B_2) remain finite for all i and q, α and β being fixed.

For the case of convergence factors of type II we obtain by specialization of Theorem II the following result:

THEOREM IV. *The necessary and sufficient conditions that the series* $\sum u_{mn} f_{mn}(\alpha)$ *converge and have its partial sums bounded for each* α *in* $E(\alpha)$, *whenever* $\sum u_{mn}$ *is summable and bounded* $(C,\, k,\, r)$, *and approach the value to which the latter series is summable as* α *approaches* α_0, *are that the convergence factors* $f_{mn}(\alpha)$ *satisfy conditions* $(A)_2$, $(B)_2$, $(D_1^{(1)})$, $(D_1^{(2)})$, $(D_2^{(1)})$, *and* $(D_2^{(2)})$ *of Theorem III and the following further conditions*:

$(A_1)_2$
$$\sum_{m=0,\,n=0}^{\infty,\infty} m^k n^r \,|\, \Delta_{k+1,r+1} f_{mn}(\alpha)\,| \; < \; K \qquad\qquad E'(\alpha),$$

$(C)_2$
$$\lim_{\alpha\to\alpha_0} f_{mn}(\alpha) \; = \; 1 \qquad (m,\, n = 0, 1, 2, \cdots),$$

(E_1)
$$\lim_{\alpha\to\alpha_0} \sum_{n=0}^{\infty} n^r \,|\, \Delta_{k+1,r+1} f_{mn}(\alpha)\,| \; = \; 0 \qquad (m = 0, 1, 2, \cdots),$$

(E_2)
$$\lim_{\alpha\to\alpha_0} \sum_{m=0}^{\infty} m^k \,|\, \Delta_{k+1,r+1} f_{mn}(\alpha)\,| \; = \; 0 \qquad (n = 0, 1, 2, \cdots),$$

where $E'(\alpha)$ is a subset of $E(\alpha)$, containing all the points of the latter set in a certain neighborhood of α_0, and K is a positive constant.

Here it is to be noted that, since we are dealing with a case where the expression (53) has only a finite number of terms, conditions $(C_1)_2$ and $(C_2)_2$ of Theorem II may be combined into condition $(C)_2$. The special case of Theorem IV where $k = r$ and the set $E(\alpha)$ lies in a space of two dimensions has been previously discussed by Moore (cf. [121], Theorem III).

4.7. Convergence factors for series summable by Cesàro means of complex orders. We may also obtain from Theorems I and II criteria for convergence factors in the case of series summable (C, k, r), where k and r are complex constants whose real components exceed zero. In this case the i and j in (53) each ranges from 0 to ∞, so that in general the $\Delta_{k+1,r+1}f_{mn}(\alpha)$ there defined is a doubly infinite series. The coefficients of its terms, however, are readily seen to satisfy equation (33).

We obtain by specialization of Theorem I:

THEOREM V. *If the series $\sum u_{mn}$ is summable and bounded (C, k, r), where k and r are complex quantities having real components σ and ρ each of which exceeds zero, the necessary and sufficient conditions that $\sum u_{mn}f_{mn}(\alpha)$ converge and have its partial sums bounded for each α in $E(\alpha)$ are that the convergence factors $f_{mn}(\alpha)$ satisfy*

$(A)_2$
$$\sum_{m=0,\,n=0}^{\infty,\infty} m^\sigma n^\rho \left| \Delta_{k+1,r+1}f_{mn}(\alpha) \right| < K(\alpha) \qquad\qquad E(\alpha),$$

$(B)_2$
$$m^\sigma n^\rho \left| f_{mn}(\alpha) \right| < M(\alpha) \qquad\qquad (E(\alpha);\ \text{all } m, n)\text{'}$$

$(D_1^{(1)})$
$$\lim_{n\to\infty} n^\rho \Delta_{k+1,0}f_{mn}(\alpha) = 0 \qquad\qquad (E(\alpha);\ \text{all } m),$$

$(D_1^{(2)})$
$$n^\rho \sum_{m=0}^{\infty} m^\sigma \left| \Delta_{k+1,0}f_{mn}(\alpha) \right| < K_1(\alpha) \qquad\qquad (E(\alpha);\ \text{all } n),$$

$(D_2^{(1)})$
$$\lim_{m\to\infty} m^\sigma \Delta_{0,r+1}f_{mn}(\alpha) = 0 \qquad\qquad (E(\alpha);\ \text{all } n),$$

$(D_2^{(2)})$
$$m^\sigma \sum_{n=0}^{\infty} n^\rho \left| \Delta_{0,r+1}f_{mn}(\alpha) \right| < K_2(\alpha) \qquad\qquad (E(\alpha);\ \text{all } m),$$

where $K(\alpha)$, $M(\alpha)$, $K_1(\alpha)$, and $K_2(\alpha)$ are positive functions of α.

In deriving the above conditions from those of Theorem I, we note that the $A_j^{(1)}$ and $A_j^{(2)}$ of conditions $(D_1^{(2)})$ and $(D_2^{(2)})$ of that theorem are in this case the coefficients of the expansions of $(1 - z)^{r+1}$ and $(1 - z)^{k+1}$ respectively, and hence they satisfy the conditions expressed by equations (31) and (32).

By specializing Theorem II we obtain criteria for convergence factors of type II in the following form:

THEOREM VI. *The necessary and sufficient conditions that the series $\sum u_{mn}f_{mn}(\alpha)$ of Theorem V shall also approach the value to which $\sum u_{mn}$ is summable and bounded*

(C, k, r) as α approaches α_0 are that the convergence factors $f_{mn}(\alpha)$, in addition to satisfying the conditions of Theorem V, satisfy the following further conditions:

$(A_1)_2$
$$\sum_{m=0,\, n=0}^{\infty,\infty} m^\sigma n^\rho \left| \Delta_{k+1,r+1} f_{mn}(\alpha) \right| < K \qquad\qquad E'(\alpha),$$

$(C_1)_2$
$$\lim_{\alpha \to \alpha_0} f_{00}(\alpha) = 1$$

$(C_2)_2$
$$\lim_{\alpha \to \alpha_0} \Delta_{k+1,r+1} f_{mn}(\alpha) = 0 \qquad (m, n = 0, 1, 2, \cdots),$$

(E_1)
$$\lim_{\alpha \to \alpha_0} \sum_{n=0}^{\infty} n^\rho \left| \Delta_{k+1,r+1} f_{mn}(\alpha) \right| = 0 \qquad (m = 0, 1, 2, \cdots),$$

(E_2)
$$\lim_{\alpha \to \alpha_0} \sum_{m=0}^{\infty} m^\sigma \left| \Delta_{k+1,r+1} f_{mn}(\alpha) \right| = 0 \qquad (n = 0, 1, 2, \cdots),$$

where $E'(\alpha)$ is a subset of $E(\alpha)$, containing all the points of the latter set in a certain neighborhood of α_0, and K is a positive constant.

CHAPTER V

CONVERGENCE FACTORS IN SUMMABLE MULTIPLE SERIES

5.1. Lemma on transformation of sequences. For any sequence to function transformation of the form

$$(1) \qquad F(\alpha) = \sum_{i_1=0}^{\infty} \cdots \sum_{i_n=0}^{\infty} s_{[i]} \, \varphi_{[i]}(\alpha),$$

we know from Lemma 3 (I) that a necessary and sufficient condition for the existence of the transformation in the case of all convergent bounded sequences is $(A^*)_n$ of 1.15. If we further wish $F(\alpha)$ to approach a limit as $\alpha \to \alpha_0$, a limit point of $E(\alpha)$ not of the set, we see by considering convergent sequences of the form $s_{[i]} = 1$, $s_{[m]} = 0$ when at least one of the m's is distinct from the corresponding i, the i's ranging through all positive integral values and zero, and also convergent sequences of the form $s_{[i]} = 1$ ($i_1, \cdots, i_n = 0, 1, 2, \cdots$), that additional necessary conditions are

$$(C_1^*)_n \qquad \qquad \lim_{\alpha \to \alpha_0} \varphi_{[i]}(\alpha) = \gamma_{[i]} \qquad \qquad \text{(all } [i]),$$

$$(C_2^*)_n \qquad \qquad \lim_{\alpha \to \alpha_0} \sum_{i_1=0}^{\infty} \cdots \sum_{i_n=0}^{\infty} \varphi_{[i]}(\alpha) = \gamma.$$

If we represent by $\sum u_{[i]}$ the infinite series whose partial sums form the given sequence and define a set of functions, $f_{[i]}(\alpha)$, in terms of the $\varphi_{[i]}(\alpha)$ by means of (50) (I), we have from (53) (I)

$$(2) \qquad F(\alpha) = \sum_{i_1=0}^{\infty} \cdots \sum_{i_n=0}^{\infty} s_{[i]} \, \Delta_{11\ldots1} f_{[i]}(\alpha) = \sum_{i_1=0}^{\infty} \cdots \sum_{i_n=0}^{\infty} u_{[i]} f_{[i]}(\alpha).$$

From this equation we can show by a discussion analogous to that used in 1.11 to establish the necessity of condition $(A_1)_2$ of Theorem V (I), that an additional necessary condition that $F(\alpha)$ approach a limit as $\alpha \to \alpha_0$, is that the $f_{[i]}(\alpha)$ satisfy $(A_1)_n$ of 1.16, and hence that the $\varphi_{[i]}(\alpha)$ satisfy the corresponding condition $(A_1^*)_n$ of 1.18. From $(A_1^*)_n$ and $(C_1^*)_n$ we obtain

$$(3) \qquad \sum_{i_1=0}^{m_1} \cdots \sum_{i_n=0}^{m_n} |\gamma_{[i]}| \leq K \qquad \qquad \text{(all } [m]),$$

and hence the series $\sum \gamma_{[i]}$ is absolutely convergent.

We next show the necessity of the n conditions $(E_s)_n$ of the type

$$(E_1)_n \qquad \lim_{\alpha \to \alpha_0} \sum_{i_1=0}^{m_1} \sum_{i_2=m_2}^{\infty} \cdots \sum_{i_n=m_n}^{\infty} |\gamma_{[i]} - \varphi_{[i]}(\alpha)| = 0 \qquad \text{(all } [m]).$$

61

The proofs being all analogous, we confine ourselves to the discussion of $(E_1)_n$. If this condition does not hold, we can find an m_1, $m_1^{(1)}$, and a positive ϵ, such that for a set of values of $(m_2, m_3, \cdots, m_n)$, there exists a set of values of α,

$$\alpha_k(m_2, m_3, \cdots, m_n) \qquad (k = 1, 2, 3, \cdots),$$

tending to α_0 and such that

(4)
$$\sum_{i_1=0}^{m_1^{(1)}} \sum_{i_2=m_2}^{\infty} \cdots \sum_{i_n=m_n}^{\infty} |\gamma_{[i]} - \varphi_{[i]}(\alpha)| > \epsilon$$

$$(\text{all } m_2, m_3, \cdots, m_n; \ \alpha = \alpha_k \ (k = 1, 2, 3, \cdots)).$$

We now select a set of values $m_2^{(1)}, m_3^{(1)}, \cdots, m_n^{(1)}$ such that

(5)
$$\sum_{i_1=0}^{m_1^{(1)}} \sum_{i_2=m_2}^{\infty} \cdots \sum_{i_n=m_n}^{\infty} |\gamma_{[i]}| < \frac{\epsilon}{10} \quad (m_2 \geqq m_2^{(1)}, \cdots, m_n \geqq m_n^{(1)}),$$

which is possible in view of the absolute convergence of $\sum \gamma_{[i]}$. We next choose one of the values of $\alpha_k(m_2^{(1)}, \cdots, m_n^{(1)})$, which we designate as $\alpha^{(1)}$. Since condition $(A^*)_n$ is satisfied, we can find a set of values $q_2^{(1)} > m_2^{(1)}, q_3^{(1)} > m_3^{(1)}, \cdots, q_n^{(1)} > m_n^{(1)}$, such that

(6)
$$\left\{ \sum_{i_1=0}^{m_1^{(1)}} \sum_{i_2=m_2^{(1)}}^{\infty} \cdots \sum_{i_n=m_n^{(1)}}^{\infty} - \sum_{i_1=0}^{m_1^{(1)}} \sum_{i_2=m_2^{(1)}}^{m_2} \cdots \sum_{i_n=m_n^{(1)}}^{m_n} \right\} |\varphi_{[i]}(\alpha^{(1)})| < \frac{\epsilon}{10}$$

$$(m_2 \geqq q_2^{(1)}, \cdots, m_n \geqq q_n^{(1)}).$$

We are going to make a choice of the $s_{[i]}$ which will lead to a contradiction by use of the above consequences of our supposition that $(E_1)_n$ is not satisfied. We first set

(7) $s_{[i]} = 0$ $(0 \leqq i_1, 0 \leqq i_2 < m_2^{(1)}, \text{ or } \cdots, \text{ or } 0 \leqq i_n < m_n^{(1)};$

$$m_1^{(1)} < i_1, m_2^{(1)} \leqq i_2, \cdots, m_n^{(1)} \leqq i_n).$$

The $s_{[i]}$ not defined by (7) will be chosen in steps, but all choices will be made in such a manner that

(8) $|s_{[i]}| \leqq 1$ $(0 \leqq i_1 \leqq m_1^{(1)}, m_2^{(1)} \leqq i_2, \cdots, m_n^{(1)} \leqq i_n).$

We now set

(9) $s_{[i]} = \text{sgn} \, [\varphi_{[i]}(\alpha^{(1)}) - \gamma_{[i]}]$

$$s_{[i]} \text{ in } \sum_{i_1=0}^{m_1^{(1)}} \left\{ \sum_{i_2=0}^{q_2^{(1)}} \cdots \sum_{i_n=0}^{q_n^{(1)}} - \sum_{i_2=0}^{m_2^{(1)}-1} \cdots \sum_{i_n=0}^{m_n^{(1)}-1} \right\}.$$

From (1), (7), and (9) we have

(10)
$$F(\alpha_1) = \sum_{i_1=0}^{m_1^{(1)}} \sum_{i_2=m_2^{(1)}}^{q_2^{(1)}} \cdots \sum_{i_n=m_n^{(1)}}^{q_n^{(1)}} \{|\varphi_{[i]}(\alpha_1) - \gamma_{[i]}| + s_{[i]}\gamma_{[i]}\}$$
$$+ \left\{ \sum_{i_1=0}^{m_1^{(1)}} \sum_{i_2=m_2^{(1)}}^{\infty} \cdots \sum_{i_n=m_n^{(1)}}^{\infty} - \sum_{i_1=0}^{m_1^{(1)}} \sum_{i_2=m_2^{(1)}}^{q_2^{(1)}} \cdots \sum_{i_n=m_n^{(1)}}^{q_n^{(1)}} \right\} s_{[i]}\varphi_{[i]}(\alpha_1).$$

From (10), (4), (5), (6), and (8) we obtain

(11)
$$F(\alpha^{(1)}) > \tfrac{6}{10}\epsilon > \tfrac{1}{2}\epsilon.$$

We next choose a set of values $m_2^{(2)} > q_2^{(1)}, \cdots, m_n^{(2)} > q_n^{(1)}$, and among the $\alpha_k(m_2^{(2)}, \cdots, m_n^{(2)})$ we select a value $\alpha^{(2)}$ nearer to α_0 than $\alpha^{(1)}$, and such that

(12)
$$\sum_{i_1=0}^{m_1^{(1)}} \sum_{i_2=m_2^{(1)}}^{m_2^{(2)}-1} \cdots \sum_{i_n=m_n^{(1)}}^{m_n^{(2)}-1} |\varphi_{[i]}(\alpha^{(2)}) - \gamma_{[i]}| < \frac{\epsilon}{10},$$

which we can do in view of $(C_1^*)_n$. We then select a set of values $q_2^{(2)} > m_2^{(2)}$, $\cdots, q_n^{(2)} > m_n^{(2)}$ such that

(13)
$$\left\{ \sum_{i_1=0}^{m_1^{(1)}} \sum_{i_2=m_2^{(1)}}^{\infty} \cdots \sum_{i_n=m_n^{(1)}}^{\infty} - \sum_{i_1=0}^{m_1^{(1)}} \sum_{i_2=m_2^{(1)}}^{m_2} \cdots \sum_{i_n=m_n^{(1)}}^{m_n} \right\} |\varphi_{[i]}(\alpha^{(2)})| < \frac{\epsilon}{10}$$
$$(m_2 \geqq q_2^{(2)}, \cdots, m_n \geqq q_n^{(2)}).$$

Then we set

(14)
$$s_{[i]} = -\text{sgn}\,[\varphi_{[i]}(\alpha^{(2)}) - \gamma_{[i]}]$$
$$s_{[i]} \text{ in } \sum_{i_1=0}^{m_1^{(1)}} \left\{ \sum_{i_2=0}^{q_2^{(2)}} \cdots \sum_{i_n=0}^{q_n^{(2)}} - \sum_{i_2=0}^{m_2^{(2)}-1} \cdots \sum_{i_n=0}^{m_n^{(2)}-1} \right\}.$$

From (1), (7), and (14) we have

(15)
$$F(\alpha^{(2)}) = \sum_{i_1=0}^{m_1^{(1)}} \sum_{i_2=m_2^{(1)}}^{m_2^{(2)}-1} \cdots \sum_{i_n=m_n^{(1)}}^{m_n^{(2)}-1} s_{[i]}(\varphi_{[i]}(\alpha^{(2)}) - \gamma_{[i]})$$
$$- \left\{ \sum_{i_1=0}^{m_1^{(1)}} \sum_{i_2=m_2^{(1)}}^{q_2} \cdots \sum_{i_n=m_n^{(1)}}^{q_n} - \sum_{i_1=0}^{m_1^{(1)}} \sum_{i_2=m_2^{(1)}}^{m_2^{(2)}-1} \cdots \sum_{i_n=m_n^{(1)}}^{m_n^{(2)}-1} \right\} |\varphi_{[i]}(\alpha^{(2)}) - \gamma_{[i]}|$$
$$+ \sum_{i_1=0}^{m_1^{(1)}} \sum_{i_2=m_2^{(1)}}^{q_2} \cdots \sum_{i_n=m_n^{(1)}}^{q_n} s_{[i]}\gamma_{[i]}$$
$$+ \left\{ \sum_{i_1=0}^{m_1^{(1)}} \sum_{i_2=m_2^{(1)}}^{\infty} \cdots \sum_{i_n=m_n^{(1)}}^{\infty} - \sum_{i_1=0}^{m_1^{(1)}} \sum_{i_2=m_2^{(1)}}^{q_2} \cdots \sum_{i_n=m_n^{(1)}}^{q_n} \right\} s_{[i]}\varphi_{[i]}(\alpha^{(2)}).$$

Combining (15) with (4), (5), (12), (13), and (8), we obtain

$$(16) \qquad F(\alpha^{(2)}) < -\tfrac{1}{2}\epsilon.$$

If we continue the choices of the $s_{[i]}$, not initially designated, in the manner indicated, we define a bounded multiple sequence converging to zero, for which $F(\alpha)$ oscillates between values $> \tfrac{1}{2}\epsilon$ and $< -\tfrac{1}{2}\epsilon$, as $\alpha \to \alpha_0$. Thus we have a contradiction, and the necessity of $(E_1)_n$ is established. As we stated before, the necessity of the other conditions $(E_s)_n$ of the same type may be proved in analogous fashion.

For any bounded, convergent sequence, $s_{[i]}$, we infer readily from (1) that if the $\varphi_{[i]}(\alpha)$ satisfy conditions $(A^*)_n$, $(A_1^*)_n$, $(C_1^*)_n$, $(C_2^*)_n$, and the n conditions of the type $(E_1)_n$, the $F(\alpha)$ defined by (1) will tend to the value of the absolutely convergent series

$$(17) \qquad \sum_{i_1=0}^{\infty} \sum_{i_2=0}^{\infty} \cdots \sum_{i_n=0}^{\infty} \gamma_{[i]} s_{[i]},$$

and the partial sums of the series in (1) will remain bounded for each α in $E(\alpha)$. If we designate the limit of $s_{[i]}$ by s and the value of the series in (17) by S, we have

$$(18) \qquad S = \lim_{\alpha \to \alpha_0} F(\alpha) = s\gamma + \sum_{i_1=0}^{\infty} \sum_{i_2=0}^{\infty} \cdots \sum_{i_n=0}^{\infty} (s_{[i]} - s)\,\gamma_{[i]}.$$

We have thus proved the following lemma:

LEMMA 1. *The necessary and sufficient conditions that the sequence to function transformation* (1), *corresponding to any bounded, convergent multiple sequence, exist in $E(\alpha)$, that the $F(\alpha)$ defined by it approach a limit as $\alpha \to \alpha_0$, and that the partial sums of the series on the right hand side of* (1) *remain bounded for each α in $E(\alpha)$, are that the $\varphi_{[i]}(\alpha)$ satisfy $(A^*)_n$, $(A_1^*)_n$, $(C_1^*)_n$, $(C_2^*)_n$, and the n conditions of type $(E_1)_n$. These conditions being satisfied, it follows that the series $\sum \gamma_{[i]}$ is absolutely convergent and the equation* (18) *subsists.*

5.2. A fundamental identity.

Corresponding to a set of $C_{[i]}$'s, defined as in 2.6, we put

$$(19) \qquad 1 \Big/ \sum_{i_1=0}^{\infty} \cdots \sum_{i_n=0}^{\infty} C_{[i]} x_1^{i_1} \cdots x_n^{i_n} \sim \sum_{i_1=0}^{\infty} \cdots \sum_{i_n=0}^{\infty} a_{[i]} x_1^{i_1} \cdots x_n^{i_n},$$

where the sign $\sim$ is used in a sense analogous to that in 3.2 and 4.2.

We have from (15) (II)

$$\sum_{i_1=0}^{\infty} \cdots \sum_{i_n=0}^{\infty} S_{[i]} x_1^{i_1} \cdots x_n^{i_n} \sim \sum s_{[i]} x_1^{i_1} \cdots x_n^{i_n} \sum c_{[i]} x_1^{i_1} \cdots x_n^{i_n}$$

$$\sim \sum u_{[i]} x_1^{i_1} \cdots x_n^{i_n} (1 - x_1)^{-1} \cdots (1 - x_n)^{-1} \sum c_{[i]} x_1^{i_1} \cdots x_n^{i_n}$$

$$\sim \sum u_{[i]} x_1^{i_1} \cdots x_n^{i_n} \sum C_{[i]} x_1^{i_1} \cdots x_n^{i_n}.$$

Hence, by use of (19),

$$\sum u_{[i]} x_1^{i_1} \cdots x_n^{i_n} \sim \frac{1}{\sum C_{[i]} x_1^{i_1} \cdots x_n^{i_n}} \sum S_{[i]} x_1^{i_1} \cdots x_n^{i_n}$$

$$\sim \sum a_{[i]} x_1^{i_1} \cdots x_n^{i_n} \sum S_{[i]} x_1^{i_1} \cdots x_n^{i_n}.$$

From this last relation we obtain

(20) $$\qquad u_{[m]} = \sum_{i_1=0}^{m_1} \cdots \sum_{i_n=0}^{m_n} a_{[i]} S_{[m-i]},$$

where we use the natural extension of our bracket notation for subscripts, whereby $[m \pm i]$ symbolizes the set of subscripts $m_1 \pm i_1$, $m_2 \pm i_2$, $\cdots$, $m_n \pm i_n$.

Corresponding to a set of functions, $f_{[i]}(\alpha)$, we define

(21) $$\quad L_{[p]} f_{[m]}(\alpha) = \sum_{i_1=0}^{p_1-m_1} \cdots \sum_{i_n=0}^{p_n-m_n} a_{[i]} f_{[m+i]}(\alpha) \qquad (p_1 \geqq m_1, \cdots, p_n \geqq m_n).$$

We readily obtain from (20) and (21) the identity

(22)
$$\sum_{m_1=0}^{p_1} \cdots \sum_{m_n=0}^{p_n} u_{[m]} f_{[m]}(\alpha) = \sum_{m_1=0}^{p_1} \cdots \sum_{m_n=0}^{p_n} S_{[m]} L_{[p]} f_{[m]}(\alpha)$$

$$= \sum_{m_1=0}^{p_1} \cdots \sum_{m_n=0}^{p_n} (S_{[m]}/C_{[m]}) C_{[m]} L_{[p]} f_{[m]}(\alpha).$$

5.3. **Convergence factors of type I.** Given a multiple series $\sum u_{[m]}$ which is summable $(N; c)$ in accordance with the definition in 2.6, and which satisfies

(23) $$\qquad\qquad | S_{[m]}/C_{[m]} | < M \qquad\qquad (M \text{ a constant; all } [m]),$$

we seek necessary and sufficient conditions on a set of functions, $f_{[m]}(\alpha)$, defined over a set $E(\alpha)$, in order that the series $\sum u_{[m]} f_{[m]}(\alpha)$ may converge in $E(\alpha)$. We see from (22) that this is equivalent to the convergence in $E(\alpha)$, as the p's become infinite, of the right hand side of (22). We may therefore obtain a set of conditions by application of Lemma 1, with $(p_1, p_2, \cdots, p_n)$ playing the rôle of α, and $\alpha_0 = (\infty, \infty, \cdots, \infty)$. Condition $(C_1^*)_n$ implies the existence of

(24) $$\quad \lim_{p_1,\cdots,p_n \to \infty} L_{[p]} f_{[m]}(\alpha) = \sum_{i_1=0}^{\infty} \cdots \sum_{i_n=0}^{\infty} a_{[i]} f_{[m+i]}(\alpha) = L f_{[m]}(\alpha) \qquad E(\alpha).$$

We have from the definition of the a's in (19)

(25) $$\qquad\qquad \sum_{i_1=0}^{p_1} \cdots \sum_{i_n=0}^{p_n} C_{[i]} L_{[p]} f_{[i]}(\alpha) = f_{[0]}(\alpha) \qquad\qquad (\text{all } [p]),$$

and therefore condition $(C_2^*)_n$, holding without further restriction, does not enter into the discussion. Conditions $(A^*)_n$ and $(A_1^*)_n$ are equivalent to

(26) $$\qquad\qquad \sum_{m_1=0}^{p_1} \cdots \sum_{m_n=0}^{p_n} | C_{[m]} L_{[p]} f_{[m]}(\alpha) | < M(\alpha),$$

$M(\alpha)$ being independent of p_1, p_2, $\cdots$, p_n. Conditions of type $(E_1)_n$ assume the typical form

$$
\lim_{p_1 \to \infty, \cdots, p_n \to \infty} \sum_{m_1=0}^{\lambda} \left\{ \sum_{m_2=r_2}^{p_2} \cdots \sum_{m_n=r_n}^{p_n} C_{[m]}[Lf_{[m]}(\alpha) - L_{[p]}f_{[m]}(\alpha)] \right.
$$
$$
\left. + \left(\sum_{m_2=r_2}^{\infty} \cdots \sum_{m_n=r_n}^{\infty} - \sum_{m_2=r_2}^{p_2} \cdots \sum_{m_n=r_n}^{p_n} \right) C_{[m]} Lf_{[m]}(\alpha) \right\} = 0
$$
$$
(E(\alpha); \text{ all } \lambda, r_2, \cdots, r_n).
$$

(27)

We thus see that (24), (26), and the n conditions of type (27) constitute a set of necessary and sufficient conditions for convergence factors of type I. We shall derive from these a more usable set, analogous to those obtained for the case of double series in Chapter IV.

We may infer from Lemma 1 or directly from (24) and (26)

$(A)_n$
$$
\sum_{m_1=0}^{\infty} \cdots \sum_{m_n=0}^{\infty} | C_{[m]} Lf_{[m]}(\alpha) | \leqq M(\alpha) < K(\alpha)
$$
$E(\alpha)$,

$K(\alpha)$ being a positive function of α, defined in $E(\alpha)$. If we replace the summation on the left hand side of (26) by the term for which $m_1 = p_1, \cdots, m_n = p_n$, we obtain

$(B)_n$
$$
| C_{[m]}f_{[m]}(\alpha) | < M(\alpha)
$$
$(E(\alpha); \text{ all } [m])$.

We now introduce the following definitions:

n definitions of the form

(28)
$$
L_1^{(1)} f_{[m]}(\alpha; i_2, \cdots, i_n) = \sum_{i_1=0}^{\infty} a_{[i]} f_{[m+i, n-1, m]}(\alpha),
$$

where by a natural extension of our bracket notation the symbol $[m + i, n - k, m]$ stands for the set of indices $m_1 + i_1, \cdots, m_k + i_k, m_{k+1}, \cdots, m_n$, and the lower index of L ranges from 1 to n, corresponding to the i that is the variable in the summation on the right and is therefore omitted as an argument on the left;

$(2^n - n - 2)$ definitions of the form

(29)
$$
L_1^{(k)} f_{[m]}(\alpha; i_{k+1}, \cdots, i_n) = \sum_{i_1=0}^{\infty} \cdots \sum_{i_k=0}^{\infty} a_{[i]} f_{[m+i, n-k, m]}(\alpha),
$$

k ranging from 2 to $(n - 1)$ inclusive, the lower index of L ranging from 1 to $\binom{n}{k}$ for each k.

We next make the following further requirements for the functions $f_{[m]}(\alpha)$:

$(2^n - 2)$ conditions $(D_s^{(k)})$ of the type

$(D_1^{(k)})$
$$
\sum_{m_1=0}^{\infty} \cdots \sum_{m_k=0}^{\infty} | C_{[m]} L_1^{(k)} f_{[m, n-k, m+i]}(\alpha; i_{k+1}, \cdots, i_n) |
$$
$$
\leqq A_1(i_{k+1}, \cdots, i_n) K_1^{(k)}(\alpha) \quad (E(\alpha); \text{ all } m_{k+1}, \cdots, m_n, i_{k+1}, \cdots, i_n),
$$

where k ranges from 1 to $(n - 1)$ inclusive and the subscript of D from 1 to $\binom{n}{k}$ for each k, while the $K_s^{(k)}(\alpha)$ are positive functions of α and the A's satisfy conditions of the form

$$(30) \qquad \sum_{i_{k+1}=0}^{\infty} \cdots \sum_{i_n=0}^{\infty} (i_{k+1} + 1) \cdots (i_n + 1) A_1(i_{k+1}, \cdots, i_n) < A_1^{(k)} < \infty ;$$

corresponding to each of the conditions $(D_s^{(1)})$ $(s = 1, 2, \cdots, n)$ a condition of the type

$$(D_1^{(1)})' \qquad \lim_{m_2 \to \infty, \cdots, m_n \to \infty} C_{[m]} L_1^{(1)} f_{[m,n-1,m+i]}(\alpha; i_2, \cdots, i_n) = 0$$

$$(E(\alpha); \text{ all } m_1, i_2, \cdots, i_n);$$

corresponding to each of the $(2^n - n - 2)$ conditions $(D_s^{(k)})$, where k ranges from 2 to $(n - 1)$, k conditions $(D_s^{(k)})_r'$ $(r = 1, \cdots, k)$ of the type

$$(D_1^{(k)})_1' \qquad \lim_{m_{k+1} \to \infty, \cdots, m_n \to \infty} \sum_{m_2=0}^{\infty} \cdots \sum_{m_k=0}^{\infty} | C_{[m]} L_1^{(k)} f_{[m,n-k,m+i]}(\alpha; i_{k+1}, \cdots, i_n) | = 0$$

$$(E(\alpha); \text{ all } m_1, i_{k+1}, \cdots, i_n).$$

We are going to show first that if the definition of summability is regular and the a's defined by (19) satisfy the supplementary condition

$$(31) \qquad \sum_{m_1=0}^{\infty} \cdots \sum_{m_n=0}^{\infty} (m_1 + 1) \cdots (m_n + 1) | a_{[m]} | < A < \infty ,$$

conditions $(A)_n$, $(B)_n$, and the various conditions $(D_s^{(k)})$, $(D_s^{(1)})'$, and $(D_s^{(k)})_r'$ will imply (24), (26), and the n relations of type (27), and may therefore be used as sufficient conditions for convergence factors of type I under the restrictions stated.

The convergence of the multiple series in (24) follows from $(B)_n$ and (31), if we take into account (17) of 2.7 and the basic assumption $c_{[0]} \neq 0$. We also make use of (17) of 2.7 to derive from $(B)_n$ a more general inequality than $(B)_n$ itself. We set

$$(32) \qquad G_{[m]} = \sum_{i_1=0}^{m_1} \cdots \sum_{i_n=0}^{m_n} | c_{[i]} |.$$

Then we have

$$(33) \qquad | C_{[m]} f_{[m+i]}(\alpha) | = \left| \frac{C_{[m]}}{C_{[m+i]}} \right| \cdot | C_{[m+i]} f_{[m+i]}(\alpha) | < \frac{G_{[m]}}{G_{[m+i]}/H} M(\alpha)$$

$$\leqq H \cdot M(\alpha) = M_1(\alpha) \qquad (E(\alpha); \text{ all } [m], [i]),$$

where $M_1(\alpha)$ is a positive function of α, defined in $E(\alpha)$.

If we can show that for each α in $E(\alpha)$

$$(34) \qquad \sum_{m_1=0}^{p_1} \cdots \sum_{m_n=0}^{p_n} C_{[m]} \{ L f_{[m]}(\alpha) - L_{[p]} f_{[m]}(\alpha) \}$$

remains bounded for all $[p]$, it will follow that (26) will hold whenever $(A)_n$ holds. We may write

(35)
$$
\begin{aligned}
Lf_{[m]}(\alpha) - L_{[p]}f_{[m]}(\alpha) = \Bigg\{ & \sum_{i_1=p_1-m_1+1}^{\infty} \cdots \sum_{i_n=p_n-m_n+1}^{\infty} \\
& + \left[\sum_{i_1=0}^{p_1-m_1} \sum_{i_2=p_2-m_2+1}^{\infty} \cdots \sum_{i_n=p_n-m_n+1}^{\infty} \right] \\
& + \left[\sum_{i_1=0}^{p_1-m_1} \sum_{i_2=0}^{p_2-m_2} \sum_{i_3=p_3-m_3+1}^{\infty} \cdots \sum_{i_n=p_n-m_n+1}^{\infty} \right] \\
& + \cdots\cdots\cdots\cdots\cdots\cdots\cdots\cdots\cdots\cdots\cdots\cdots\cdots\cdots \\
& + \left[\sum_{i_1=0}^{p_1-m_1} \cdots \sum_{i_{n-1}=0}^{p_{n-1}-m_{n-1}} \sum_{i_n=p_n-m_n+1}^{\infty} \right] \Bigg\} \, a_{[i]} f_{[m+i]}(\alpha),
\end{aligned}
$$

where the brackets around a set of summation signs indicate that we include also all other combinations of summations, of which the particular one given is a typical example. To be more explicit, the first bracket indicates all sets of summations where one of the i's ranges from zero to the corresponding $(p-m)$, while the other $(n-1)$ i's range from the corresponding $(p-m+1)$ to ∞; the significance of the remaining brackets is analogous.

It follows readily from (33) and (31) that the portion of the expression in (34) corresponding to the first summation on the right hand side of (35) remains finite for all choices of $[p]$, α having any fixed value in $E(\alpha)$. The discussion of the contribution to the expression (34) arising from the various summations bracketed in (35) may be adequately indicated by considering the case where the first k summations are from zero to the appropriate $(p-m)$, the remaining $(n-k)$ summations from the appropriate $(p-m+1)$ to ∞. We have

(36)
$$
\begin{aligned}
& \sum_{m_1=0}^{p_1} \cdots \sum_{m_k=0}^{p_k} C_{[m]} \sum_{i_1=0}^{p_1-m_1} \cdots \sum_{i_k=0}^{p_k-m_k} a_{[i]} f_{[m+i]}(\alpha) \\
& = \sum_{m_1=0}^{p_1} \cdots \sum_{m_k=0}^{p_k} C_{[m]} \Bigg\{ L_1^{(k)} f_{[m,n-k,m+i]}(\alpha; i_{k+1}, \cdots, i_n) \\
& \qquad - \left[\sum_{i_k=p_k-m_k+1}^{\infty} L_1^{(k-1)} f_{[m,n-k+1,m+i]}(\alpha; i_k, \cdots, i_n) \right] \\
& \qquad - \cdots\cdots\cdots\cdots\cdots\cdots\cdots\cdots\cdots\cdots\cdots\cdots\cdots\cdots\cdots\cdots \\
& \qquad - \left[\sum_{i_2=p_2-m_2+1}^{\infty} \cdots \sum_{i_k=p_k-m_k+1}^{\infty} L_1^{(1)} f_{[m,n-1,m+i]}(\alpha; i_2, \cdots, i_n) \right] \\
& \qquad - \sum_{i_1=p_1-m_1+1}^{\infty} \cdots \sum_{i_k=p_k-m_k+1}^{\infty} a_{[i]} f_{[m+i]}(\alpha) \Bigg\},
\end{aligned}
$$

where the brackets indicate that we include all L's with the same upper index, defined by summations involving the proper number of i's chosen among the first k, the summations before the L's involving the remaining i's of this set.

From (36) we obtain

$$\left| \sum_{m_1=0}^{p_1} \cdots \sum_{m_n=0}^{p_n} C_{[m]} \sum_{i_1=0}^{p_1-m_1} \cdots \sum_{i_k=0}^{p_k-m_k} \sum_{i_{k+1}=p_{k+1}-m_{k+1}+1}^{\infty} \cdots \sum_{i_n=p_n-m_n+1}^{\infty} a_{[i]} f_{[m+i]}(\alpha) \right|$$

$$\leq \left| \sum_{m_1=0}^{p_1} \cdots \sum_{m_n=0}^{p_n} C_{[m]} \sum_{i_{k+1}=p_{k+1}-m_{k+1}+1}^{\infty} \cdots \right.$$

$$\left. \sum_{i_n=p_n-m_n+1}^{\infty} L_1^{(k)} f_{[m,n-k,m+i]}(\alpha; i_{k+1}, \cdots, i_n) \right|$$

$$+ \left[\left| \sum_{m_1=0}^{p_1} \cdots \sum_{m_n=0}^{p_n} C_{[m]} \sum_{i_k=p_k-m_k+1}^{\infty} \cdots \right. \right.$$

(37)

$$\left. \left. \sum_{i_n=p_n-m_n+1}^{\infty} L_1^{(k-1)} f_{[m,n-k+1,m+i]}(\alpha; i_k, \cdots, i_n) \right| \right]$$

$$+ \cdots \cdots \cdots \cdots \cdots \cdots \cdots \cdots \cdots \cdots \cdots \cdots \cdots \cdots \cdots \cdots \cdots$$

$$+ \left[\left| \sum_{m_1=0}^{p_1} \cdots \sum_{m_n=0}^{p_n} C_{[m]} \sum_{i_2=p_2-m_2+1}^{\infty} \cdots \right. \right.$$

$$\left. \left. \sum_{i_n=p_n-m_n+1}^{\infty} L_1^{(1)} f_{[m,n-1,m+i]}(\alpha; i_2, \cdots, i_n) \right| \right]$$

$$+ \left| \sum_{m_1=0}^{p_1} \cdots \sum_{m_n=0}^{p_n} C_{[m]} \sum_{i_1=p_1-m_1+1}^{\infty} \cdots \sum_{i_n=p_n-m_n+1}^{\infty} a_{[i]} f_{[m+i]}(\alpha) \right|,$$

where the brackets have the same significance as in (36). The boundedness of each term but the last on the right hand side of (37), for all choices of the p's, follows readily from the various $(D_s^{(k)})$'s and (30). The boundedness of the last term follows from (33) and (31).

We may thus regard as established the boundedness of (34) for all choices of the p's, the α having any fixed value in $E(\alpha)$. Hence, for a regular definition of summability such that (31) is satisfied, (26) follows from $(A)_n$ and the $(D_s^{(k)})$.

In view of $(A)_n$ the derivation of relations of the type (27) reduces to the derivation of relations of the type

$$\lim_{p_1 \to \infty, \cdots, p_n \to \infty} \sum_{m_1=0}^{\lambda} \sum_{m_2=r_2}^{p_2} \cdots \sum_{m_n=r_n}^{p_n} C_{[m]} \left\{ L f_{[m]}(\alpha) - L_{[p]} f_{[m]}(\alpha) \right\} = 0$$

(38)

$$(E(\alpha); \text{ all } \lambda, r_2, \cdots, r_n).$$

It follows from (33) and (31) that the contribution to the summation on the left hand side of (38) corresponding to the first summation on the right hand side of (35), will for a fixed $\lambda, r_2, \cdots, r_n$, and α tend to zero as p_1 becomes infinite, uniformly in $p_2, \cdots, p_n$. In analogy with the procedure used in the establishment of (26), the discussion of the contributions to the summation in (38) corresponding to the various summations which are bracketed in (35) may be adequately indicated by considering the case where the first k summations are from zero to the appropriate $(p - m)$, the remaining $(n - k)$ summations from the appropriate $(p - m + 1)$ to ∞. It follows, if we take account of (36), that for the contribution to the summation in (38) corresponding to the case in question we have an inequality of the same type as (37), where the only change is that the first n summations on the left hand side and in each term on the right hand side have the following range $(0, \lambda; r_2, p_2; \cdots; r_n, p_n)$. That for a fixed $\lambda, \alpha, r_2, \cdots, r_n$ the last term on the right hand side of this inequality tends to zero uniformly in $p_2, \cdots, p_n$ as $p_1 \to \infty$, follows readily from (33) and (31). The discussion of the various other terms on the right hand side may be indicated adequately by considering the first term.

It follows from condition $(D_1^{(k)})$ that, corresponding to a positive ϵ and a fixed $\lambda, \alpha, r_2, \cdots, r_n$, we can choose a set of values, $m_{k+1}^{(1)}, \cdots, m_n^{(1)}$ such that for $p_{k+1} \geq m_{k+1}^{(1)} + r_{k+1}, \cdots, p_n \geq m_n^{(1)} + r_n$, we have

$$(39) \quad \left| \sum_{m_1=0}^{\lambda} \sum_{m_2=r_2}^{p_2} \cdots \sum_{m_k=r_k}^{p_k} \sum_{m_{k+1}=p_{k+1}-m_{k+1}^{(1)}+1}^{p_{k+1}} \cdots \sum_{m_n=p_n-m_n^{(1)}+1}^{p_n} C_{[m]} \right.$$
$$\left\{ \sum_{i_{k+1}=p_{k+1}-m_{k+1}+1}^{\infty} \cdots \sum_{i_n=p_n-m_n+1}^{\infty} - \sum_{i_{k+1}=p_{k+1}-m_{k+1}+1}^{m_k^{(1)}} \cdots \sum_{i_n=p_n-m_n+1}^{m_n^{(1)}} \right\}$$
$$\left. L_1^{(k)} f_{[m,n-k,m+i]}(\alpha; i_{k+1}, \cdots, i_n) \right| < \frac{\epsilon}{3},$$

$$(40) \quad \left| \left\{ \sum_{m_1=0}^{\lambda} \sum_{m_2=r_2}^{p_2} \cdots \sum_{m_n=r_n}^{p_n} - \sum_{m_1=0}^{\lambda} \sum_{m_2=r_2}^{p_2} \cdots \sum_{m_k=r_k}^{p_k} \sum_{m_{k+1}=p_{k+1}-m_{k+1}^{(1)}+1}^{p_{k+1}} \right. \right.$$
$$\left. \cdots \sum_{m_n=p_n-m_n^{(\cdot)}+1}^{p_n} \right\} C_{[m]} \sum_{i_{k+1}=p_{k+1}-m_{k+1}+1}^{\infty} \cdots \sum_{i_n=p_n-m_n+1}^{\infty}$$
$$\left. L_1^{(k)} f_{[m,n-k,m+i]}(\alpha; i_{k+1}, \cdots, i_n) \right| < \frac{\epsilon}{3}.$$

Then, in view of condition $(D_1^{(k)})_1'$, we can choose a set of values, $p_{k+1}^{(1)} \geq m_{k+1}^{(1)} + r_{k+1}, \cdots, p_n^{(1)} \geq m_n^{(1)} + r_n$, such that

$$(41) \quad \left| \sum_{m_1=0}^{\lambda} \sum_{m_2=r_2}^{p_2} \cdots \sum_{m_k=r_k}^{p_k} \sum_{m_{k+1}=p_{k+1}-m_{k+1}^{(1)}+1}^{p_{k+1}} \cdots \sum_{m_n=p_n-m_n^{(1)}+1}^{p_n} \right.$$
$$\left. C_{[m]} \sum_{i_{k+1}=p_{k+1}-m_{k+1}+1}^{m_{k+1}^{(1)}} \cdots \sum_{i_n=p_n-m_n+1}^{m_n^{(1)}} L_1^{(k)} f_{[m,n-k,m+i]}(\alpha; i_{k+1}, \cdots, i_n) \right| < \frac{\epsilon}{3}.$$

Combining (41) with (39), and the result with (40), we see that the first term on the right hand side of the inequality corresponding to (37) can be made as small as we please by choosing $p_{k+1}, \cdots, p_n$ sufficiently large. As indicated before, the treatment of this term is typical of the treatment of other terms on the right hand side of the inequality, except for the last term which has been previously discussed. Furthermore, the discussion of the inequality corresponding to (37) illustrates adequately the discussion of the various contributions to the summation in (38), arising from the summations which are bracketed in (35), as we have indicated previously. We may therefore regard (38), and hence (27), as established. Since the other relations, of which (27) is typical, may be obtained in analogous fashion, we may conclude that (24), (26), and the n conditions of type (27) follow from conditions $(A)_n$, $(B)_n$, and the various conditions $(D_s^{(k)})$, $(D_s^{(1)})'$, and $(D_s^{(k)})'_r$. The latter set of conditions are therefore sufficient conditions for convergence factors of type I. We take up next the discussion of their necessity.

5.4. Necessity of the conditions. We are seeking conditions that will at the same time be necessary and sufficient for all definitions of the type considered, and therefore we are at liberty to introduce special forms of such definitions in connection with the necessity proofs when need arises. This remark should be kept in mind when reading the proof of the necessity of conditions of the type $(D_s^{(k)})$, given subsequently.

Since $(A)_n$ is a consequence of the necessary conditions (24) and (26), and $(B)_n$ is implied by the necessary condition (26), the necessity of $(A)_n$ and $(B)_n$ is established.

The proofs of the necessity of $(D_s^{(1)})'$ and $(D_s^{(k)})'_r$ $(k = 2, \cdots, n)$, are all of the same general type, and each follows in its main outlines the proof of the necessity of $(D_1^{(1)})$ in Chapter IV. The changes in detail that must be introduced to meet the more general situation will be sufficiently indicated by writing out the proof of the necessity of $(D_1^{(k)})'_k$ for a general k in the range $(2, \cdots, n)$.

We have from (22) and (29)

$$\sum_{m_1=0}^{p_1} \cdots \sum_{m_n=0}^{p_n} u_{[m]} f_{[m]}(\alpha)$$

$$(42) \quad \begin{aligned} &= \sum_{m_1=0}^{p_1} \cdots \sum_{m_n=0}^{p_n} S_{[m]} \sum_{i_{k+1}=0}^{p_{k+1}-m_{k+1}} \cdots \sum_{i_n=0}^{p_n-m_n} L_1^{(k)} f_{[m,n-k,m+i]}(\alpha; i_{k+1}, \cdots, i_n) \\[2mm] &\quad - \sum_{m_1=0}^{p_1} \cdots \sum_{m_n=0}^{p_n} S_{[m]} \sum_{i_{k+1}=0}^{p_{k+1}-m_{k+1}} \cdots \sum_{i_n=0}^{p_n-m_n} \\[2mm] &\quad\quad\quad \left\{ \sum_{i_1=0}^{\infty} \cdots \sum_{i_k=0}^{\infty} - \sum_{i_1=0}^{p_1-m_1} \cdots \sum_{i_k=0}^{p_k-m_k} \right\} a_{[i]} f_{[m+i]}(\alpha). \end{aligned}$$

If $(D_1^{(k)})'_k$ does not hold for some particular value of α, we can find an $\epsilon > 0$, an $m_k^{(1)}$, and a set of λ's $(\lambda_{k+1}, \cdots, \lambda_n)$, such that

$$(43) \quad \sum_{m_1=0}^{\infty} \cdots \sum_{m_{k-1}=0}^{\infty} \left| C_{[m]} \sum_{i_{k+1}=0}^{\lambda_{k+1}} \cdots \sum_{i_n=0}^{\lambda_n} L_1^{(k)} f_{[m,n-k,m+i]}(\alpha; i_{k+1}, \cdots, i_n) \right| > \epsilon$$

$$(m_k = m_k^{(1)})$$

for an infinite number of choices of the set of indices $m_{k+1}, \cdots, m_n$. Let us indicate these choices by $m_{k+1}^{(s)}, \cdots, m_n^{(s)}$ $(s = 1, 2, 3, \cdots)$.

We now take $p_r^{(1)} = m_r^{(1)} + \lambda_r \ (r = k+1, \cdots, n)$, and $p_j^{(1)} \ (j = 1, \cdots, k-1)$ sufficiently large to make

(44)
$$\sum_{m_1=0}^{p_1^{(1)}} \cdots \sum_{m_{k-1}=0}^{p_{k-1}^{(1)}} \left| C_{[m]} \sum_{i_{k+1}=0}^{\lambda_{k+1}} \cdots \sum_{i_n=0}^{\lambda_n} L_1^{(k)} f_{[m,n-k,m+i]}(\alpha; i_{k+1}, \cdots, i_n) \right| > \epsilon$$

$$(m_r = m_r^{(1)}; r = k, \cdots, n),$$

which is possible in view of (43). We further choose $p_k^{(1)} > m_k^{(1)}$ and sufficiently large to have

(45)
$$\left| \sum_{m_1=0}^{p_1^{(1)}} \cdots \sum_{m_{k-1}=0}^{p_{k-1}^{(1)}} C_{[m]} \sum_{i_{k+1}=0}^{p_{k+1}^{(1)}-m_{k+1}} \cdots \sum_{i_n=0}^{p_n^{(1)}-m_n} \left\{ \sum_{i_1=0}^{\infty} \cdots \sum_{i_k=0}^{\infty} - \sum_{i_1=0}^{p_1^{(1)}-m_1} \cdots \sum_{i_k=0}^{p_k^{(1)}-m_k} \right\} a_{[i]} f_{[m+i]}(\alpha) \right| < \tfrac{1}{2}\epsilon$$

$$(m_r = m_r^{(1)}; r = k, \cdots, n).$$

The possibility of this latter choice we infer from $(B)_n$, already proved necessary, and (31).

We then choose

(46)
$$S_{[m,n-k+1,m^{(1)}]} = \left| C_{[m,n-k+1,m^{(1)}]} \right| \qquad (0 \leq m_r \leq p_r^{(1)}; r = 1, \cdots, k-1),$$
$$S_{[m]} = 0 \qquad \text{(all other sets of indices in } (0 \leq m_j \leq p_j^{(1)}; j = 1, \cdots, n)).$$

We next take $p_r^{(2)} = m_r^{(2)} + \lambda_r \ (r = k+1, \cdots, n)$, and $p_j^{(2)} \ (j = 1, \cdots, k-1)$ sufficiently large to have

(47)
$$\sum_{m_1=0}^{p_1^{(2)}} \cdots \sum_{m_{k-1}=0}^{p_{k-1}^{(2)}} \left| C_{[m]} \sum_{i_{k+1}=0}^{\lambda_{k+1}} \cdots \sum_{i_n=0}^{\lambda_n} L_1^{(k)} f_{[m,n-k,m+i]}(\alpha; i_{k+1}, \cdots, i_n) \right| > \epsilon$$

$$(m_k = m_k^{(1)}; m_r = m_r^{(2)} \ (r = k+1, \cdots, n)).$$

We then choose $p_k^{(2)} > p_k^{(1)}$ and sufficiently large to make

(48)
$$\left| \sum_{m_1=0}^{p_1^{(1)}} \cdots \sum_{m_{k-1}=0}^{p_{k-1}^{(1)}} C_{[m]} \sum_{i_{k+1}=0}^{p_{k+1}^{(2)}-m_{k+1}} \cdots \sum_{i_n=0}^{p_n^{(2)}-m_n} \left\{ \sum_{i_1=0}^{\infty} \cdots \sum_{i_k=0}^{\infty} - \sum_{i_1=0}^{p_1^{(2)}-m_1} \cdots \sum_{i_k=0}^{p_k^{(2)}-m_k} \right\} a_{[i]} f_{[m+i]}(\alpha) \right| < \tfrac{1}{4}\epsilon$$

$$(m_k = m_k^{(1)}; m_r = m_r^{(1)} \text{ or } m_r^{(2)} \ (r = k+1, \cdots, n)).$$

We now set

$$P_1 = \sum_{m_1=0}^{p_1^{(1)}} \cdots \sum_{m_{k-1}=0}^{p_{k-1}^{(1)}} S_{[m]} \sum_{i_{k+1}=0}^{\lambda_{k+1}} \cdots \sum_{i_n=0}^{\lambda_n} L_1^{(k)} f_{[m,n-k,m+i]}(\alpha; i_{k+1}, \cdots, i_n)$$

$$(m_r = m_r^{(1)}; r = k, \cdots, n),$$

$$P_2 = \sum_{m_1=0}^{p_1^{(1)}} \cdots \sum_{m_{k-1}=0}^{p_{k-1}^{(1)}} S_{[m]} \sum_{i_{k+1}=0}^{p_{k+1}^{(2)}-m_{k+1}} \cdots \sum_{i_n=0}^{p_n^{(2)}-m_n} L_1^{(k)} f_{[m,n-k,m+i]}(\alpha; i_{k+1}, \cdots, i_n).$$

If $P_2 \neq P_1$, we put

(49)
$$S_{[m,n-k,m^{(2)}]} = | C_{[m,n-k,m^{(2)}]} | \, \text{sgn} \sum_{i_{k+1}=0}^{\lambda_{k+1}}$$

$$\cdots \sum_{i_n=0}^{\lambda_n} L_1^{(k)} f_{[m,n-k,m+i]}(\alpha; i_{k+1}, \cdots, i_n) \frac{P_2 - P_1}{| P_2 - P_1 |}$$

$$(0 \leq m_r \leq p_r^{(2)} \ (r = 1, \cdots, k-1; m_k = m_k^{(1)})),$$

and we further set $S_{[m]} = 0$ for all other sets of indices in the range $(0 \leq m_j \leq p_j; j = 1, \cdots, n)$, not included in the definitions (46) and (49). If $P_2 = P_1$, we omit the indeterminate factor $(P_2 - P_1)/| P_2 - P_1 |$ in (49), everything else remaining the same.

It is readily seen that if we continue our choice of the p's and our definition of the S's in accordance with the procedure indicated above, the first term on the right hand side of (42) will have an oscillation whose absolute value exceeds ϵ for each new set of p's, whereas the second term will remain in absolute value less than $\frac{1}{2}\epsilon$. Since the series $\sum u_{[m]}$ corresponding to our choice of the S's will be summable $(N; c)$ to zero, we have here a contradiction which establishes the necessity of $(D_1^{(k)})_k'$. As indicated before, the proofs of all the other conditions of type (D)' are analogous to that just given.

We take up next the proof of the necessity of conditions of the type $(D_s^{(k)})$. We shall discuss in particular condition $(D_1^{(k)})$, the proofs for the other cases being analogous. To deal with this case we consider a situation where the a's of (19) take the form

(50) $$a_{[m]} = A(m_1, \cdots, m_k) A_1(m_{k+1}, \cdots, m_n).$$

If we then set

(51) $$L_k f_{[m]}(\alpha) = \sum_{i_1=0}^{\infty} \cdots \sum_{i_k=0}^{\infty} A(i_1, \cdots, i_k) f_{[m+i,n-k,m]}(\alpha),$$

we have from (29)

(52) $$L_1^{(k)} f_{[m]}(\alpha; i_{k+1}, \cdots, i_n) = A_1(i_{k+1}, \cdots, i_n) L_k f_{[m]}(\alpha).$$

It follows from (31) and (50) that the A_1's of (52) satisfy (30). Hence, in order to prove the necessity of $(D_1^{(k)})$, we need to show that

$$(53) \qquad \sum_{m_1=0}^{\infty} \cdots \sum_{m_k=0}^{\infty} \mid C_{[m]} L_k f_{[m,n-k,m+i]}(\alpha) \mid \; \leqq K_1^{(k)}(\alpha)$$

$$(E(\alpha); \text{ all } m_{k+1}, \cdots, m_n)$$

must hold for all sets of $(i_{k+1}, \cdots, i_n)$ for which $A_1(i_{k+1}, \cdots, i_n) \neq 0$. If (53) does not hold for some value of α in $E(\alpha)$, we can find a set $(m_{k+1}^{(1)}, \cdots, m_n^{(1)})$ and a set $(i_{k+1}^{(1)}, \cdots, i_n^{(1)})$ for which $A_1(i_{k+1}^{(1)}, \cdots, i_n^{(1)}) \neq 0$, such that

$$(54) \qquad \sum_{m_1=0}^{p_1} \cdots \sum_{m_k=0}^{p_k} \mid C_{[m,n-k,m^{(1)}]} L_k f_{[m,n-k,m^{(1)}+i^{(1)}]}(\alpha) \mid$$

increases indefinitely as $p_1, \cdots, p_k$ become infinite by taking on a set of values $p_1^{(r)}, \cdots, p_k^{(r)}$ $(r = 1, 2, \cdots)$.

If we set

$$(55) \qquad \sigma_{[p]}(\alpha) = \sum_{m_1=0}^{p_1} \cdots \sum_{m_n=0}^{p_n} u_{[m]} f_{[m]}(\alpha),$$

we have from (42), taking $p_j^{(1)} = m_j^{(1)} + i_j^{(1)}$ $(j = k+1, \cdots, n)$, and setting $S_{[m]} = 0$, whenever $m_j \neq m_j^{(1)}$ for any value of j from $(k+1)$ to n inclusive

$$(-1)^{n-k} \Delta_{0,1}^{k,n-k} \sigma_{[p,n-k,p^{(1)}-1]}$$

$$(56) \qquad = A_1(i_{k+1}^{(1)}, \cdots, i_n^{(1)}) \sum_{m_1=0}^{p_1} \cdots \sum_{m_k=0}^{p_k} S_{[m,n-k,m^{(1)}]} L_k f_{[m,n-k,m^{(1)}+i^{(1)}]}(\alpha)$$

$$- A_1(i_{k+1}^{(1)}, \cdots, i_n^{(1)}) \sum_{m_1=0}^{p_1} \cdots \sum_{m_k=0}^{p_k} S_{[m,n-k,m^{(1)}]} \left\{ \sum_{i_1=0}^{\infty} \cdots \sum_{i_k=0}^{\infty} - \sum_{i_1=0}^{p_1-m_1} \cdots \sum_{i_k=0}^{p_k-m_k} \right\}$$

$$A(i_1, \cdots, i_k) f_{[m+i,n-k,m^{(1)}+i^{(1)}]}(\alpha),$$

where the Δ symbol on the left hand side has the same significance as in (41) of Chapter I.

We now put

$$(57) \qquad S_{[m,n-k,m^{(1)}]} = \mid C_{[m,n-k,m^{(1)}]} \mid \operatorname{sgn} L_k f_{[m,n-k,m^{(1)}+i^{(1)}]}(\alpha)$$

$$(\text{all } m_s; \; s = 1, 2, \cdots, k).$$

We then infer from (33) and (31) that the second term on the right hand side of (56) remains bounded as $p_1, \cdots, p_k$ become infinite; on the other hand from the fact that (54) becomes infinite as the r in $p_1^{(r)}, \cdots, p_k^{(r)}$ takes on the values $1, 2, \cdots$, we conclude that the same is true for the first term on the right hand side of (56). Hence the $\sigma_{[p]}(\alpha)$, defined by (55), do not form a bounded sequence when the u's on the right hand side correspond to S's defined by (57) and by setting $S_{[m]} = 0$ for all combinations of indices not listed in (57). This contradiction establishes the necessity of $(D_1^{(k)})$, and as pointed out before the proof of the necessity is analogous for all other conditions $(D_s^{(k)})$.

We have now established both the sufficiency and the necessity of $(A)_n$, $(B)_n$, and the various conditions $(D_s^{(1)})'$, $(D_s^{(k)})'_r$, and $(D_s^{(k)})$ for convergence factors of type I. We therefore have the following theorem:

THEOREM I. *The necessary and sufficient conditions for all definitions $(N; c)$ which are regular and satisfy the supplementary condition (31) that the series $\sum u_{[m]} f_{[m]}(\alpha)$ shall converge in $E(\alpha)$ and that its partial sums shall form a bounded sequence for each α in $E(\alpha)$, whenever the series $\sum u_{[m]}$ is summable $(N; c)$ and satisfies (23), are that the convergence factors should satisfy $(A)_n$, $(B)_n$, and the various conditions $(D_s^{(k)})$, $(D_s^{(1)})'$, and $(D_s^{(k)})'_r$.*

5.5. Convergence factors of type II. We seek next necessary and sufficient conditions that the series $\sum u_{[m]} f_{[m]}(\alpha)$ should also approach the value to which the series $\sum u_{[m]}$ is summable $(N; c)$ as $\alpha \to \alpha_0$, a limit point of $E(\alpha)$, not of the set. If the convergence factors, $f_{[m]}(\alpha)$, satisfy the conditions of Theorem I, we have from (22), (24), (25), and (18), using the notations of 2.6,

$$\sum_{m_1=0}^{\infty} \cdots \sum_{m_n=0}^{\infty} u_{[m]} f_{[m]}(\alpha)$$

$$(58) \qquad = \sigma f_{[0]}(\alpha) + \sum_{m_1=0}^{\infty} \cdots \sum_{m_n=0}^{\infty} (\sigma_{[m]} - \sigma) C_{[m]} L f_{[m]}(\alpha)$$

$$= \sum_{m_1=0}^{\infty} \cdots \sum_{m_n=0}^{\infty} \sigma_{[m]} C_{[m]} L f_{[m]}(\alpha) \qquad\qquad E(\alpha).$$

If we apply Theorem IX (I) to the sequence to function transformation defined by the right hand side of (58), we see that the necessary and sufficient conditions, in addition to those of Theorem I, that the expression in question should tend to σ as $\alpha \to \alpha_0$, are

$$(A_1)_n \qquad\qquad \sum_{m_1=0}^{\infty} \cdots \sum_{m_n=0}^{\infty} |C_{[m]} L f_{[m]}(\alpha)| < K \qquad\qquad E'(\alpha),$$

where K is a positive constant and $E'(\alpha)$ is a subset of $E(\alpha)$, having α_0 as a limit point,

$$(C_1)_n \qquad\qquad \lim_{\alpha \to \alpha_0} f_{[0]}(\alpha) = 1,$$

$$(C_2)_n \qquad\qquad \lim_{\alpha \to \alpha_0} L f_{[m]}(\alpha) = 0 \qquad\qquad (\text{all } [m]),$$

and the n conditions $(E_s)_n$, of type

$$(E_1)_n \qquad\qquad \lim_{\alpha \to \alpha_0} \sum_{m_2=0}^{\infty} \cdots \sum_{m_n=0}^{\infty} |C_{[m]} L f_{[m]}(\alpha)| = 0 \qquad (\text{all } [m]).$$

We have thus established:

THEOREM II. *The necessary and sufficient conditions for all definitions $(N; c)$ which are regular and satisfy the supplementary condition (31), that the series*

$\sum u_{[m]} f_{[m]}(\alpha)$ converge in $E(\alpha)$ and have its partial sums bounded for each α, whenever $\sum u_{[m]}$ is summable $(N; c)$ and satisfies (23), and furthermore approach the value to which the latter series is summable as α approaches α_0, are that the functions $f_{[m]}(\alpha)$ satisfy conditions $(A)_n$, $(A_1)_n$, $(B)_n$, $(C_1)_n$, $(C_2)_n$, and the various conditions $(D_s^{(k)})$, $(D_s^{(1)})'$, $(D_s^{(k)})'_r$, and $(E_s)_n$.

5.6. Convergence factor theorems for Cesàro means of integral orders.
If we set

$$(59) \qquad c_{[m]} = c_{m_1}^{(r_1)} c_{m_2}^{(r_2)} \cdots c_{m_n}^{(r_n)},$$

where the c's on the right hand side are defined as in (19) (III), we have the case of Cesàro summability for n-tuple series. Considering first the case where the r's in (59) are positive integers, we have from (59) and (24)

$$(60) \quad \begin{aligned} Lf_{[m]}(\alpha) &= \Delta_{[r+1]} f_{[m]}(\alpha) \\ &= \sum_{i_1=0}^{r_1+1} \cdots \sum_{i_n=0}^{r_n+1} (-1)^{i_1} \cdots (-1)^{i_n} \binom{r_1+1}{r_1+1-i_1} \cdots \binom{r_n+1}{r_n+1-i_n} f_{[m]}(\alpha). \end{aligned}$$

We then have as a special case of Theorem I the following result:

THEOREM III. *The necessary and sufficient conditions that the series* $\sum u_{[m]} f_{[m]}(\alpha)$ *shall converge and have its partial sums bounded for each α in $E(\alpha)$ whenever the series* $\sum u_{[m]}$ *is summable and bounded $(C, r_1, \cdots, r_n)$, the r's being positive integers, are that the functions $f_{[m]}(\alpha)$ satisfy*

$$(A)_n \qquad \sum_{m_1=0}^{\infty} \cdots \sum_{m_n=0}^{\infty} m_1^{r_1} \cdots m_n^{r_n} |\Delta_{[r+1]} f_{[m]}(\alpha)| < K(\alpha) \qquad E(\alpha),$$

$$(B)_n \qquad m_1^{r_1} \cdots m_n^{r_n} |f_{[m]}(\alpha)| < M(\alpha) \qquad (E(\alpha); \text{ all } m_1, \cdots, m_n),$$

$(2^n - 2)$ *conditions* $(D_s^{(k)})$ *of the form*

$$(D_1^{(k)}) \quad m_{k+1}^{r_{k+1}} \cdots m_n^{r_n} \sum_{m_1=0}^{\infty} \cdots \sum_{m_k=0}^{\infty} m_1^{r_1} \cdots m_k^{r_k} |\Delta_{[r+1,n-k,0]} f_{[m]}(\alpha)| < K_1^{(k)}(\alpha) \quad E(\alpha),$$

corresponding to each of the n conditions $(D_s^{(1)})$ $(s = 1, 2, \cdots, n)$ *a condition* $(D_s^{(1)})'$ *of the type*

$$(D_1^{(1)})' \qquad \lim_{m_2 \to \infty, \cdots, m_n \to \infty} m_2^{r_2} \cdots m_n^{r_n} \Delta_{[r+1,n-1,0]} f_{[m]}(\alpha) = 0 \qquad (E(\alpha); \text{ all } m_1),$$

corresponding to each of the $(2^n - n - 2)$ conditions $(D_s^{(k)})$ $(k = 2, \cdots, n-1)$ *k conditions* $(D_s^{(k)})'_j$ *of the form*

$$(D_1^{(k)})'_1 \quad \begin{aligned} &\lim_{m_{k+1} \to \infty, \cdots, m_n \to \infty} m_{k+1}^{r_{k+1}} \cdots m_n^{r_n} \\ &\sum_{m_2=0}^{\infty} \cdots \sum_{m_k=0}^{\infty} m_2^{r_2} \cdots m_k^{r_k} |\Delta_{[r+1,n-k,0]} f_{[m]}(\alpha)| = 0 \qquad (E(\alpha); \text{ all } m_1), \end{aligned}$$

where $K(\alpha)$, $M(\alpha)$, and the various $K_s^{(k)}(\alpha)$ are all positive functions of α, defined over $E(\alpha)$.

In specializing Theorem I we have taken advantage of the simplifications which arise from the fact that the L's occurring in the conditions of Theorem I are in the present case finite sums and that the rate of increase of the C's as functions of the m's is known. These simplifications are analogous to those in the case of double series, which are specified just after the statement of Theorem III (IV) in 4.6.

Turning to the case of convergence factors of type II we obtain by specialization of Theorem II the result below:

THEOREM IV. *The necessary and sufficient conditions that the series $\sum u_{[m]} f_{[m]}(\alpha)$ converge and have its partial sums bounded for each α in $E(\alpha)$, whenever $\sum u_{[m]}$ is summable and bounded $(C, r_1, \cdots, r_n)$, and approach the value to which the latter series is summable as α approaches α_0, are that the convergence factors $f_{[m]}(\alpha)$ satisfy conditions $(A)_n$, $(B)_n$, the various conditions $(D_s^{(k)})$, $(D_s^{(1)})'$, $(D_s^{(k)})'_j$ of Theorem III, and the following further conditions:*

$(A_1)_n$
$$\sum_{m_1=0}^{\infty} \cdots \sum_{m_n=0}^{\infty} m_1^{r_1} \cdots m_n^{r_n} \left| \Delta_{[r+1]} f_{[m]}(\alpha) \right| < K \qquad E'(\alpha),$$

$(C)_n$
$$\lim_{\alpha \to \alpha_0} f_{[m]}(\alpha) = 1 \qquad (\text{all } m_j; j = 1, \cdots, n),$$

n conditions (E_s) of the type

(E_1)
$$\lim_{\alpha \to \alpha_0} \sum_{m_2=0}^{\infty} \cdots \sum_{m_n=0}^{\infty} m_2^{r_2} \cdots m_n^{r_n} \left| \Delta_{[r+1]} f_{[m]}(\alpha) \right| = 0 \qquad (\text{all } m_1),$$

where $E'(\alpha)$ is a subset of $E(\alpha)$ containing all the points of the latter set in a certain neighborhood of α_0, and K is a positive constant.

The fact that the $\Delta_{[r+1]} f_{[m]}(\alpha)$ has only a finite number of terms enables us to combine conditions $(C_1)_n$ and $(C_2)_n$ into the single condition $(C)_n$.

5.7. Convergence factors for series summable by Cesàro means of complex orders. We may likewise obtain from Theorems I and II criteria for convergence factors in the case of series summable $(C, r_1, \cdots, r_n)$, where the r's are complex constants whose real components exceed zero. The $\Delta_{[r+1]} f_{[m]}(\alpha)$, defined by (60), is in this case an n-tuply infinite series, but the coefficients of its terms are readily seen to satisfy equation (31).

We obtain from Theorem I:

THEOREM V. *If the series $\sum u_{[m]}$ is summable and bounded $(C, r_1, \cdots, r_n)$, where the $r_j (j = 1, \cdots, n)$ are complex quantities having real components $\rho_j (j = 1, \cdots, n)$, each of which exceeds zero, the necessary and sufficient conditions that $\sum u_{[m]} f_{[m]}(\alpha)$ converge and have its partial sums bounded for each α in $E(\alpha)$ are that the convergence factors $f_{[m]}(\alpha)$ satisfy*

$(A)_n$
$$\sum_{m_1=0}^{\infty} \cdots \sum_{m_n=0}^{\infty} m_1^{\rho_1} \cdots m_n^{\rho_n} \left| \Delta_{[r+1]} f_{[m]}(\alpha) \right| < K(\alpha) \qquad E(\alpha),$$

$(B)_n$
$$m_1^{\rho_1} \cdots m_n^{\rho_n} \left| f_{[m]}(\alpha) \right| < M(\alpha) \qquad (E(\alpha); \text{all } m_1, \cdots, m_n),$$

$(2^n - 2)$ *conditions* $(D_s^{(k)})$ *of the form*

$$(D_1^{(k)}) \quad m_{k+1}^{\rho k+1} \cdots m_n^{\rho n} \sum_{m_1=0}^{\infty} \cdots \sum_{m_k=0}^{\infty} m_1^{\rho 1} \cdots m_k^{\rho k} \left| \Delta_{[r+1,n-m,0]} f_{[m]}(\alpha) \right| < K_1^{(k)}(\alpha)$$

$$(E(\alpha); \text{ all } m_{k+1}, \cdots, m_n),$$

n *conditions* $(D_s^{(1)})'$ *of the form*

$$(D_1^{(1)})' \quad \lim_{m_2\to\infty,\cdots,m_n\to\infty} m_2^{\rho 2} \cdots m_n^{\rho n} \Delta_{[r+1,n-1,0]} f_{[m]}(\alpha) = 0 \qquad (E(\alpha); \text{ all } m_1),$$

corresponding to each of the $(2^n - n - 2)$ *conditions* $(D_s^{(k)})$ $(k = 2, \cdots, n-1)$, k *conditions* $(D_s^{(k)})'_j$ *of the form*

$$(D_1^{(k)})'_j \quad \lim_{m_{k+1}\to\infty,\cdots,m_n\to\infty} m_{k+1}^{\rho k+1} \cdots m_n^{\rho n} \sum_{m_2=0}^{\infty} \cdots \sum_{m_n=0}^{\infty} m_2^{\rho 2} \cdots m_n^{\rho n} \left| \Delta_{[r+1,n-k,0]} f_{[m]}(\alpha) \right|$$

$$= 0 \quad (E(\alpha); \text{ all } m_1),$$

where $K(\alpha)$, $M(\alpha)$, *and the various* $K_s^{(k)}(\alpha)$ *are all positive functions of* α.

In obtaining the conditions of Theorem V from those of Theorem I, we note that constants of the form $A_i(i_{k+1}, \cdots, i_n)$, occurring in conditions $(D_s^{(k)})$ are coefficients in the expansions in power series of expressions of the form

$$(1 - z_{k+1})^{r_{k+1}} \cdots (1 - z_n)^{r_n+1}$$

and that therefore they satisfy conditions of the form (30).

From Theorem II we obtain the following criteria for convergence factors of type II:

THEOREM VI. *The necessary and sufficient conditions that the series* $\sum u_{[m]} f_{[m]}(\alpha)$ *shall approach the value to which* $\sum u_{[m]}$ *is summable* $(C, r_1, \cdots, r_n)$, *the latter series being also bounded* $(C, r_1, \cdots, r_n)$, *as* α *approaches* α_0, *are that the convergence factors* $f_{[m]}(\alpha)$, *satisfying the conditions of Theorem V, should also satisfy*

$$(A_1)_n \qquad \sum_{m_1=0}^{\infty} \cdots \sum_{m_n=0}^{\infty} m_1^{\rho 1} \cdots m_n^{\rho n} \left| \Delta_{[r+1]} f_{[m]}(\alpha) \right| < K \qquad E'(\alpha),$$

$$(C_1)_n \qquad \lim_{\alpha\to\alpha_0} f_{[0]}(\alpha) = 1,$$

$$(C_2)_n \qquad \lim_{\alpha\to\alpha_0} \Delta_{[r+1]} f_{[m]}(\alpha) = 0 \qquad (\text{all } m_1, \cdots, m_n),$$

and n *conditions* (E_s) *of the type*

$$(E_1) \qquad \lim_{\alpha\to\alpha_0} \sum_{m_2=0}^{\infty} \cdots \sum_{m_n=0}^{\infty} m_2^{\rho 2} \cdots m_n^{\rho n} \left| \Delta_{[r+1]} f_{[m]}(\alpha) \right| = 0 \qquad (\text{all } m_1),$$

where $E'(\alpha)$ *is a subset of* $E(\alpha)$, *containing all the points of the latter set in a certain neighborhood of* α_0, *and* K *is a positive constant.*

CHAPTER VI

CONVERGENCE FACTORS IN RESTRICTEDLY CONVERGENT MULTIPLE SERIES

6.1. Restrictedly convergent double sequences and series. We begin with some definitions and notations. For each θ in the interval $0 < \theta < 1$ we shall designate as the "θ-portion" of a double sequence[21] (s_{mn}) the aggregate of elements for which

(1) $$\theta n < m < \theta^{-1} n \text{ or, equivalently, } \theta m < n < \theta^{-1} m.$$

If s_{mn} tends to a limit as m and n become infinite in such a manner that the corresponding elements of the double sequence all lie in the θ-portion, we shall represent this limit by

(2) $$\lim_{\{m,n \to \infty; \theta\}} s_{mn}.$$

If the limit (2) exists and has the same value for each θ in the interval $0 < \theta < 1$, we say that the sequence (s_{mn}) is restrictedly convergent, and we designate such a limit by

(3) $$\{\lim_{m,n \to \infty}\} s_{mn}.$$

For sequences whose elements are all real, we use the notations

(4) $$\overline{\lim_{\{m,n \to \infty; \theta\}}} s_{mn}, \qquad \underline{\lim_{\{m,n \to \infty; \theta\}}} s_{mn}$$

to designate the upper and lower limits, when these are finite, which we obtain by allowing m and n to become infinite under the restriction that the s_{mn} all lie in the θ-portion of the sequence (s_{mn}). If the first limit in (4) exists for each θ in $0 < \theta < 1$ and has a least upper bound for such values of θ, or if the second limit exists and has a greatest lower bound in the same θ-interval, we designate these bounds as

(5) $$\{\overline{\lim}\}_{m,n \to \infty} s_{mn}, \qquad \{\underline{\lim}\}_{m,n \to \infty} s_{mn}.$$

If, corresponding to a double series $\sum u_{mn}$, the limit (3) exists for the sequence formed from its partial sums, we say that the double series is restrictedly convergent[22] to the value of that limit. It is apparent that a double series converg-

---

[21] Cf. Lösch [109], p. 37.
[22] Cf. Moore [117], p. 567.

ent in the general sense is also restrictedly convergent, but the converse is not true.

It is desirable to have a notation, analogous to (3) in the case of sequences, to indicate that a double series is summed in the restricted manner. We shall accordingly define

(6) $$\left\{\sum_{i=0,j=0}^{\infty,\infty}\right\} u_{ij} = \{\lim_{m,n\to\infty}\} \sum_{i=0,j=0}^{m,n} u_{ij},$$

whenever the limit on the right hand side exists.

6.2. Convergence factors of type I for restrictedly convergent double series. It is natural to inquire as to what change, if any, takes place in the convergence factor theorems of Chapter I, if we specify only restricted convergence for the series $\sum u_{mn}$ and seek to infer restricted convergence for the series $\sum u_{mn}f_{mn}(\alpha)$. It is readily seen that in the case of convergence factors of type I this change in hypothesis and conclusion involves no change in the necessary and sufficient conditions on the convergence factors, $f_{mn}(\alpha)$, formulated in Theorem IV (I). For, if we refer back to the identity (20) (I) and the discussion of the various terms on the right hand side of this identity, given in 1.7, we note that the only property of the s_{ij} used in discussing the first three terms was their boundedness for all i, j. These terms therefore converge, and the second and third of them to zero, even if s_{pq} converges only in the restricted sense. In the case of the fourth term, the convergence of s_{pq} to zero insured the convergence of this term to zero and therefore the convergence of the left hand side. Likewise, in the case of the weakened hypothesis of the restricted convergence of s_{pq} to zero, we may infer the restricted convergence of the fourth term to zero and therefore the restricted convergence of the left hand side.

Thus we see that the conditions on the convergence factors, imposed in Theorem IV (I), remain sufficient for the case of restricted convergence. In the proof of the necessity of these conditions in 1.8, the specific series used are all restrictedly convergent, and the series with convergence factors fail to be restrictedly convergent. The conditions of Theorem IV (I), therefore, remain necessary and sufficient in the present instance.

In 1.9 the condition $(A^*)_2$ was obtained as the necessary and sufficient condition for the existence of a sequence to function transformation of a bounded, convergent double sequence. This result was obtained by use of Theorem IV (I), Lemma 2 (I) thus appearing as a consequence of that theorem. In the same manner we may infer in the present instance that condition $(A^*)_2$ of Chapter I is the necessary and sufficient condition that a sequence to function transformation, exist in $E(\alpha)$ for the class of restrictedly convergent, bounded sequences.

6.3. Convergence factors of type II for restrictedly convergent double series. We shall first show by an example that if the series $\sum u_{mn}$ is only restrictedly convergent to a value s, the conditions of Theorem V (I) are not sufficient that the series $\sum u_{mn}f_{mn}(\alpha)$ shall approach the value s as α approaches α_0.

For this purpose we consider the double series defined by

$$u_{0q^2} = (-1)^q, \qquad u_{qq^2} = (-1)^{q+1} \qquad\qquad (q = 1, 2, \cdots),$$

(7)

$$u_{mn} = 0 \qquad\qquad\qquad \text{(all other } m, n).$$

If, for any θ in the interval $0 < \theta < 1$, we choose $p > \theta^{-1}$, we readily see that

(8) $s_{mn} = 0$ $(m \geqq p, n \geqq p^2 ; \theta m < n < \theta^{-1} m).$

For if $p^2 \leqq q^2 \leqq n < (q + 1)^2$, we must have $m > q$ in order that the condition for restricted convergence, expressed by the last inequality in (8), should hold. Hence the series defined by (7) is restrictedly convergent; it is also evident from (7) that the partial sums of the series remain bounded. However, the series is not convergent in the general sense, since s_{q-1,q^2} oscillates as q becomes infinite.

We now take the $E(\alpha)$ of Theorem V (I) as a set of points $\alpha_1 , \alpha_2 , \cdots , \alpha_k , \cdots$, such that there exists

(9) $$\lim_{k\to\infty} \alpha_k = \alpha_0.$$

We then define

(10)
$$f_{mn}(\alpha_k) = 1 \qquad (0 \leqq m \leqq k - 1, 0 \leqq n \leqq k^2)$$
$$\qquad\qquad\qquad\qquad\qquad\qquad\qquad (k = 1, 2, \cdots).$$
$$f_{mn}(\alpha_k) = 0 \qquad (m \geqq k \text{ or } n > k^2)$$

It is readily verified that the functions (10) satisfy all the conditions of Theorem V (I). If these functions are introduced as factors into the terms of (7), we see at once that

$$\sum u_{mn} f_{mn}(\alpha_k) = (-1)^k \qquad\qquad (k = 1, 2, \cdots),$$

and therefore does not approach a limit as α_k approaches α_0 .

It is evident from the above example that we must supplement the conditions of Theorem V (I), if we wish to obtain criteria for convergence factors of type II for the case of restrictedly convergent double series. The supplementary conditions adequate for this purpose are found to take the form

(F₁) $$\varlimsup_{\alpha\to\alpha_0} \sum_{j=0}^{\infty} \sum_{i=0}^{[\theta j]} | \Delta_{11} f_{ij}(\alpha) | \to 0 \text{ as } \theta \to 0,$$

(F₂) $$\varlimsup_{\alpha\to\alpha_0} \sum_{i=0}^{\infty} \sum_{j=0}^{[\theta i]} | \Delta_{11} f_{ij}(\alpha) | \to 0 \text{ as } \theta \to 0,$$

where we use $[x]$ as in the theory of numbers to indicate the greatest integer $\leqq x$.

Corresponding to any double series $\sum u_{ij}$, converging restrictedly to zero and having bounded partial sums, we may obtain from (20) (I) an identity of the form

(11) $$\left\{ \sum_{i=0,j=0}^{\infty,\infty} \right\} u_{ij} f_{ij}(\alpha) = \left\{ \sum_{i=0,j=0}^{\infty,\infty} \right\} s_{ij} \Delta_{11} f_{ij}(\alpha) = \sum_{i=0,j=0}^{\infty,\infty} s_{ij} \Delta_{11} f_{ij}(\alpha),$$

provided the convergence factors, $f_{ij}(\alpha)$, satisfy the conditions of Theorem IV (I). For, as was pointed out in 6.1, the fourth term on the right hand side of

(20) (I) converges in the restricted sense to zero, and the other terms converge in the general sense, the second and third to zero.

We wish to show now that if the s_{ij} in (11) form a bounded sequence for which

$$\{\lim_{i,j \to \infty}\} s_{ij} = 0,$$

and the convergence factors, $f_{ij}(\alpha)$, satisfy conditions (F$_1$) and (F$_2$), in addition to the requirements of Theorem V (I), the right hand member of (11) will tend to zero as α approaches α_0 .

Corresponding to a given positive ϵ, we can, in view of (F$_1$) and (F$_2$), choose a θ such that

(12)
$$\overline{\lim_{\alpha \to \alpha_0}} \sum_{j=0}^{\infty} \sum_{i=0}^{[\theta j]} | \Delta_{11} f_{ij}(\alpha) | < \frac{\epsilon}{5C},$$

$$\overline{\lim_{\alpha \to \alpha_0}} \sum_{i=0}^{\infty} \sum_{j=0}^{[\theta i]} | \Delta_{11} f_{ij}(\alpha) | < \frac{\epsilon}{5C},$$

the C being defined as in (17) (I). In view of relations (12), we can choose a set $E_1(\alpha)$, included in the set $E'(\alpha)$ of condition (A$_1$)$_2$ of 1.10, such that

(13)
$$\sum_{j=0}^{\infty} \sum_{i=0}^{[\theta j]} | \Delta_{11} f_{ij}(\alpha) | < \frac{\epsilon}{4C}$$

$$\sum_{i=0}^{\infty} \sum_{j=0}^{[\theta i]} | \Delta_{11} f_{ij}(\alpha) | < \frac{\epsilon}{4C}$$

$$E_1(\alpha).$$

On account of the restricted convergence of s_{ij} to zero, we can choose an m and an n such that

(14)
$$| s_{ij} | < \frac{\epsilon}{4K} \qquad (i > m, j > n; \theta j < i < \theta^{-1} j),$$

where the K is the K of condition (A$_1$)$_2$ of 1.10.

We now divide the summation of the right hand member of (11) into four partial summations, $\Sigma_1(\alpha)$, $\Sigma_2(\alpha)$, $\Sigma_3(\alpha)$, and $\Sigma_4(\alpha)$, the indices of whose terms range in the following manner:

(Σ_1) $\theta j < i < \theta^{-1} j; 0 < i \leqq m$ or $0 < j \leqq n$,

(Σ_2) $\theta j < i < \theta^{-1} j; i > m$ and $j > n$,

(Σ_3) $0 \leqq i \leqq \theta j; 0 \leqq j$,

(Σ_4) $0 \leqq j \leqq \theta i; 0 < i$.

From (13) and (17) (I), we have

(15)
$$| \Sigma_3(\alpha) | < \frac{\epsilon}{4}, \qquad | \Sigma_4(\alpha) | < \frac{\epsilon}{4} \qquad\qquad E_1(\alpha).$$

From (14) and condition $(A_1)_2$ of Theorem V (I), we have

(16) $$|\Sigma_2(\alpha)| < \frac{\epsilon}{4} \qquad\qquad E'(\alpha).$$

It follows from conditions (E_1) and (E_2) of Theorem V (I) and (17) (I) that we can choose a set $E_2(\alpha)$, included in $E_1(\alpha)$, and therefore in $E'(\alpha)$, such that

(17) $$|\Sigma_1(\alpha)| < \frac{\epsilon}{4} \qquad\qquad E_2(\alpha).$$

Combining (15), (16), and (17), we have

(18) $$\left|\left\{\sum_{i=0,j=0}^{\infty,\infty}\right\} u_{ij}f_{ij}(\alpha)\right| = \left|\sum_{i=0,j=0}^{\infty,\infty} s_{ij}\Delta_{11}f_{ij}(\alpha)\right| < \epsilon \qquad E_2(\alpha),$$

and therefore we may conclude that the conditions of Theorem V (I), with the supplementary conditions (F_1) and (F_2), are sufficient for convergence factors of type II in the case of double series converging restrictedly to zero and having bounded partial sums. Since any restrictedly convergent double series can be reduced to this case by alteration of the term in the upper left hand corner, we may regard the sufficiency of our conditions as proved in general.

6.4. **Necessity of the conditions.** The conditions of Theorem V (I) were proved necessary for convergence factors of type II in 1.8 and 1.11. The series used in these proofs are all restrictedly convergent, and hence the proofs referred to serve to establish the necessity of these same conditions when we confine ourselves to the class of restrictedly convergent double series. It remains to prove the necessity of the supplementary conditions, (F_1) and (F_2).

Since the proofs for the two cases are entirely analogous, we shall confine ourselves to the case of (F_1). If (F_1) does not hold, we can find a positive ϵ such that

(19) $$\sum_{j=0}^{\infty}\sum_{i=0}^{[\theta j]}|\Delta_{11}f_{ij}(\alpha)| > 5\epsilon$$

for a set of values of θ $(\theta_1, \theta_2, \cdots, \theta_k, \cdots)$, tending to zero as a limit, and a corresponding set of values of α $(\alpha_1, \alpha_2, \cdots, \alpha_k, \cdots)$, tending to α_0 as a limit. Among the successive values of θ, θ_k, we choose one, $\theta^{(1)}$, and we represent by $\alpha^{(1)}$ the corresponding value of α. Then we choose n_1 such that

(20) $$\sum_{j=0}^{n_1}\sum_{i=0}^{[\theta^{(1)}j]}|\Delta_{11}f_{ij}(\alpha^{(1)})| > 4\epsilon,$$

which is possible, in view of (19). We then define

(21) $$s_{ij} = \operatorname{sgn}\Delta_{11}f_{ij}(\alpha^{(1)}) \qquad (0 \leq j \leq n_1, 0 \leq i \leq \theta^{(1)}j).$$

We next choose $p_1 > n_1$ and such that

(22) $$\sum_{j=p_1}^{\infty}\sum_{i=0}^{[\theta^{(1)}j]}|\Delta_{11}f_{ij}(\alpha^{(1)})| < \epsilon,$$

which is possible, in view of condition $(A)_2$ of Theorem V (I), previously shown to be necessary. Then if we define

(23) $$s_{ij} = 0 \qquad (n_1 < j < p_1, 0 \leqq i \leqq \theta^{(1)}j),$$

and further agree that all other s_{ij} whose indices lie in the range $(0 \leqq j < \infty,$ $0 \leqq i \leqq \theta^{(1)}j)$ shall have values whose absolute value is unity or zero, while all remaining s_{ij} $(0 \leqq i, 0 \leqq j)$ are taken equal to zero, we have from (20), (21), (22), and (23)

(24) $$\left| \sum_{i=0,j=0}^{\infty,\infty} s_{ij} \Delta_{11} f_{ij}(\alpha^{(1)}) \right| > 3\epsilon.$$

We now proceed with the definition of the s_{ij} whose indices lie in the range $(0 \leqq j < \infty, 0 \leqq i \leqq \theta^{(1)}j)$, and which have not been explicitly defined. We first choose from the α_k a particular value $\alpha^{(2)}$ that lies beyond $\alpha^{(1)}$ in the set and is such that

(25) $$\sum_{j=0}^{n_1} \sum_{i=0}^{[\theta^{(1)}j]} | \Delta_{11} f_{ij}(\alpha^{(2)}) | < \frac{\epsilon}{2},$$

which is possible, in view of condition (C_2) of Theorem V (I). We also choose $q_1 > p_1$ and such that

(26) $$\sum_{j=q_1}^{\infty} \sum_{i=0}^{[\theta^{(1)}j]} | \Delta_{11} f_{ij}(\alpha^{(2)}) | < \frac{\epsilon}{2}.$$

If now we set

(27) $$s_{ij} = 0 \qquad (p_1 \leqq j \leqq q_1, 0 \leqq i \leqq \theta^{(1)}j),$$

it being understood as before that the remaining s's, not yet defined, have each an absolute value that does not exceed unity, we have from (25) and (26)

(28) $$\left| \sum_{i=0,j=0}^{\infty,\infty} s_{ij} \Delta_{11} f_{ij}(\alpha^{(2)}) \right| < \epsilon.$$

We now choose from the sequence α_k a value $\alpha^{(3)}$ which lies beyond $\alpha^{(2)}$ and is such that

(29) $$\sum_{j=0}^{q_1} \sum_{i=0}^{[\theta^{(1)}j]} | \Delta_{11} f_{ij}(\alpha^{(3)}) | < \epsilon,$$

and we represent by $\theta^{(3)}$ the corresponding value of θ. Then we choose $n_3 > q_1$ and such that

(30) $$\sum_{j=0}^{n_3} \sum_{i=0}^{[\theta^{(3)}j]} | \Delta_{11} f_{ij}(\alpha^{(3)}) | > 4\epsilon,$$

which is possible in view of (19), and we further choose $p_3 > n_3$ and such that

(31) $$\sum_{j=p_3}^{\infty} \sum_{i=0}^{[\theta^{(3)}j]} | \Delta_{11} f_{ij}(\alpha^{(3)}) | < \epsilon.$$

We then set

(32)
$$s_{ij} = \operatorname{sgn} \Delta_{11} f_{ij}(\alpha^{(3)}) \quad (q_1 < j < p_3, 0 \leqq i \leqq \theta^{(3)} j),$$
$$s_{ij} = 0 \qquad (q_1 < j < p_3, \theta^{(3)} j < i \leqq \theta^{(1)} j),$$

it being understood that all s's with values not yet assigned are chosen not to exceed unity in absolute value. We then have from (29), (30), (31), and (32)

(33)
$$\left| \sum_{i=0,j=0}^{\infty,\infty} s_{ij} \Delta_{11} f_{ij}(\alpha^{(3)}) \right| > 2\epsilon.$$

We next choose from the α_k a value $\alpha^{(4)}$ lying beyond $\alpha^{(3)}$ in the sequence and such that

(34)
$$\sum_{j=0}^{p_3} \sum_{i=0}^{[\theta^{(1)}j]} |\Delta_{11} f_{ij}(\alpha^{(4)})| < \frac{\epsilon}{2},$$

and we choose $q_3 > p_3$ and such that

(35)
$$\sum_{j=q_3}^{\infty} \sum_{i=0}^{[\theta^{(1)}j]} |\Delta_{11} f_{ij}(\alpha^{(4)})| < \frac{\epsilon}{2}.$$

If then we set

(36)
$$s_{ij} = 0 \qquad (p_3 \leqq j \leqq q_3, 0 \leqq i \leqq \theta^{(1)} j),$$

and make the same assumption as before regarding the s's with values not yet assigned, we have from (34), (35), and (36)

(37)
$$\left| \sum_{i=0,j=0}^{\infty,\infty} s_{ij} \Delta_{11} f_{ij}(\alpha^{(4)}) \right| < \epsilon.$$

It is now apparent that if we continue to choose the s's with values yet unassigned in accordance with the plan indicated above, the absolute value of the right hand member of (11) will oscillate continually between values $> 2\epsilon$ and values $< \epsilon$, while α takes on the values $\alpha^{(1)}, \alpha^{(2)}, \alpha^{(3)}, \alpha^{(4)}, \cdots$. But the series corresponding to the choice of the s's is restrictedly convergent to zero. Hence the necessity of (F_1), and therefore of (F_2), is demonstrated.

We thus have the theorem:

THEOREM I.   *The necessary and sufficient conditions that the series $\sum u_{mn} f_{mn}(\alpha)$ shall be restrictedly convergent in $E(\alpha)$ whenever the series $\sum u_{mn}$ has this property, and that the value of the former series shall approach that of the latter series as α approaches α_0, are that the convergence factors, $f_{mn}(\alpha)$, should satisfy the conditions of Theorem V (I) and the supplementary conditions (F_1) and (F_2).*

6.5. **Sequence to function transformations.**   We pointed out in 6.2 that the condition $(A^*)_2$ was necessary and sufficient for the convergence in $E(\alpha)$ of $\sum s_{ij} \varphi_{ij}(\alpha)$, whenever s_{ij} is bounded and restrictedly convergent. To find the necessary and sufficient conditions that $\sum s_{ij} \varphi_{ij}(\alpha)$ shall also approach the value to which s_{ij} converges as α approaches α_0, we apply Theorem I to the related series with convergence factors, $\sum u_{ij} f_{ij}(\alpha)$, where $f_{ij}(\alpha)$ is defined in terms of the $\varphi_{ij}(\alpha)$ by means of (25) (I), and then transform the conditions of Theorem I into conditions involving the $\varphi_{ij}(\alpha)$ by means of the relations (27) (I). This leads to the following theorem:

THEOREM II. *The necessary and sufficient conditions that for every bounded and restrictedly convergent double sequence (s_{ij}) the series $\sum s_{ij} \varphi_{ij}(\alpha)$ shall converge in $E(\alpha)$ and shall approach the value to which the double sequence converges in the restricted manner as α approaches α_0, are that the functions $\varphi_{ij}(\alpha)$ satisfy the conditions of Theorem VI (I) and the following supplementary conditions*

(F_1^*) $$\varlimsup_{\alpha \to \alpha_0} \sum_{j=0}^{\infty} \sum_{i=0}^{[\theta j]} |\varphi_{ij}(\alpha)| \to 0 \text{ as } \theta \to 0,$$

(F_2^*) $$\varlimsup_{\alpha \to \alpha_0} \sum_{i=0}^{\infty} \sum_{j=0}^{[\theta i]} |\varphi_{ij}(\alpha)| \to 0 \text{ as } \theta \to 0.$$

A special case of Theorem II of particular importance results when we consider transformations of the type

(38) $$\sigma_{mn} = \sum_{i=0, j=0}^{m, n} a_{mnij} s_{ij} \qquad (m, n = 0, 1, 2, \cdots).$$

If we inquire as to the necessary and sufficient conditions that the sequence (σ_{mn}) shall be restrictedly convergent, whenever the bounded sequence (s_{mn}) is restrictedly convergent, and to the same value, we obtain by specialization of Theorem II the following set of conditions:

There exists an m_1 and an n_1 and a positive constant K such that

$(\mathrm{A}_1^*)_2$ $$\sum_{i=0, j=0}^{m, n} |a_{mnij}| < K \qquad (m \geqq m_1, n \geqq n_1, \theta m < n < \theta^{-1} m, 0 < \theta < 1),$$

(E_1^*) $$\{\lim\}_{m, n \to \infty} \sum_{j=0}^{n} |a_{mnij}| = 0 \qquad \text{(each } i),$$

(E_2^*) $$\{\lim\}_{m, n \to \infty} \sum_{i=0}^{m} |a_{mnij}| = 0 \qquad \text{(each } j),$$

$(\mathrm{C})_2$ $$\{\lim\}_{m, n \to \infty} \sum_{i=0, j=0}^{m, n} a_{mnij} = 1,$$

(F_1^*) $$\varlimsup_{\{m, n \to \infty; \theta\}} \sum_{j=0}^{n} \sum_{i=0}^{[\theta j]} |a_{mnij}| \to 0 \text{ as } \theta \to 0 \qquad (0 < \theta < 1),$$

(F_2^*) $$\varlimsup_{\{m, n \to \infty; \theta\}} \sum_{i=0}^{m} \sum_{j=0}^{[\theta i]} |a_{mnij}| \to 0 \text{ as } \theta \to 0 \qquad (0 < \theta < 1).$$

Among transformations of the form (38) we have those of factorable type,

(39) $$a_{mnij} = \alpha_{mi} \beta_{nj}.$$

We know from Theorem III (I) that the α_{mi} and β_{nj} will yield regular transformations of simply infinite sequences if they satisfy the following conditions:

$$\sum_{i=0}^{m} |\alpha_{mi}| < K \text{ (all } m\text{)}, \qquad \sum_{j=0}^{n} |\beta_{nj}| < K \text{ (all } n\text{)},$$

(40)
$$\lim_{m \to \infty} \alpha_{mi} = 0 \text{ (each } i\text{)}, \qquad \lim_{n \to \infty} \beta_{nj} = 0 \text{ (each } j\text{)},$$

$$\lim_{m \to \infty} \sum_{i=0}^{m} \alpha_{mi} = 1, \qquad \lim_{n \to \infty} \sum_{j=0}^{n} \beta_{nj} = 1.$$

It is natural to inquire as to whether or not the a_{mnij} of (39) will satisfy the conditions obtained from Theorem II, when the α_{mi} and β_{nj} satisfy (40). It is readily seen that the first four conditions hold, but we can show by simple examples that the last two are not always satisfied. For example, if we set

$$\beta_{nn} = 1, \qquad \beta_{nj} = 0 \qquad (j = 0, 1, \cdots, n - 1),$$

$$\alpha_{i^2, i} = 1, \qquad \alpha_{mi} = 0 \qquad \text{(all other } m, i\text{)},$$

we see that (F_1^*) does not hold, and a corresponding example with the rôles of the α and β reversed gives us a case where (F_2^*) fails to be satisfied. We must therefore add to the conditions (40) two conditions obtained by specializing (F_1^*) and (F_2^*) to the case (39). These supplementary conditions are then the necessary and sufficient conditions that a transformation of the form (38) where the a_{mnij} are defined as in (39) and the α's and β's satisfy (40), should serve as a regular transformation in the domain of restrictedly convergent double sequences. This is one of the results due to Lösch [109; §II].

6.6. **Restrictedly convergent multiple sequences and series.** In analogy with the definitions and notations of 6.1, we shall, for each θ in $0 < \theta < 1$, designate as the "θ-portion" of an n-tuple sequence $(s_{[i]})$ the aggregate of elements for which

(41)
$$\theta i_k < i_j < \theta^{-1} i_k \qquad (k \neq j; k, j = 1, 2, \cdots, n).$$

If $s_{[i]}$ tends to a limit as $i_1, i_2, \cdots, i_n$ become infinite in such a manner that the corresponding elements of the multiple sequence all lie in the θ-portion, we shall designate this limit as

(42)
$$\lim_{\{i_1, \cdots, i_n \to \infty; \theta\}} s_{[i]}.$$

If the limit (42) exists and has the same value for each θ in the interval $0 < \theta < 1$, we say that the sequence $(s_{[i]})$ is restrictedly convergent, or in notation

(43)
$$\{\lim_{i_1, \cdots, i_n \to \infty}\} s_{[i]}.$$

For sequences whose elements are all real, we use the notations,

(44)
$$\varlimsup_{\{i_1, \cdots, i_n \to \infty; \theta\}} s_{[i]}, \qquad \varliminf_{\{i_1, \cdots, i_n \to \infty; \theta\}} s_{[i]},$$

to designate the upper and lower limits, when these exist, which we obtain by allowing $i_1, \cdots, i_n$ to become infinite under the restriction that the $s_{[i]}$ all lie in the θ-portion of the sequence $s_{[i]}$. If the first limit in (44) exists for each θ in $0 < \theta < 1$ and has a least upper bound for such values of θ, or if the second limit exists and has a greatest lower bound in the same θ-interval, we designate these bounds as

$$(45) \qquad \{\overline{\lim}\}_{i_1,\cdots,i_n\to\infty} s_{[i]}, \qquad \{\underline{\lim}\}_{i_1,\cdots,i_n\to\infty} s_{[i]}.$$

If, corresponding to an n-tuple series, $\sum u_{[i]}$, the limit (43) exists for the sequence formed from its partial sums, we say that the n-tuple series is restrictedly convergent to the value of that limit. To indicate that an n-tuple series is summed in the restricted manner, we use the notation

$$(46) \qquad \{\sum_{i_1=0}^{\infty} \cdots \sum_{i_n=0}^{\infty}\} u_{[i]} = \{\lim\}_{m_1,\cdots,m_n\to\infty} \sum_{i_1=0}^{m_1} \cdots \sum_{i_n=0}^{m_n} u_{[i]}.$$

6.7. Convergence factors of type I for restrictedly convergent multiple series. In 6.2 we showed, by use of the identity (20) (I), that the necessary and sufficient conditions for convergence factors of type I in double series remained unchanged when we limited ourselves to the domain of restrictedly convergent double series. That is to say we proved that the field of convergence factors which serve to convert a restrictedly convergent double series with bounded sums into one with the same property is identical with the field of convergence factors for double series with bounded sums convergent in the general manner. An entirely analogous result holds in the case of multiple series, and it is readily obtained in a similar fashion by use of the identity (40) (I). The only term on the right hand side of that identity whose discussion is altered by the limitation to restricted convergence is the last term, and that term will converge restrictedly to zero when $s_{[m]}$ does. Thus the conditions of Theorem VII (I) are sufficient in the case of restricted convergence, and the proof of their necessity remains valid under this hypothesis.

Likewise we can show that the necessary and sufficient condition for the existence of a sequence to function transformation in the case of convergent, bounded sequences, namely condition $(A^*)_n$ of Lemma 3 (I), remains a necessary and sufficient condition when we limit ourselves to the domain of restrictedly convergent, bounded sequences.

6.8. Convergence factors of type II for restrictedly convergent multiple series. When we turn to the case of convergence factors of type II, it is apparent from our results in the case of double series that we shall need to add to the conditions of Theorem VIII (I) certain supplementary conditions of the same general nature as conditions (F_1) and (F_2) of Theorem I. These conditions are found to be the $n(n-1)$ conditions $(F_k^{(r)})$ of the type

$$(F_1^{(2)}) \qquad \overline{\lim}_{\alpha\to\alpha_0} \sum_{i_2=0}^{\infty} \cdots \sum_{i_n=0}^{\infty} \sum_{i_1=0}^{[\theta i_2]} |\Delta_{[1]} f_{[i]}(\alpha)| \to 0 \text{ as } \theta \to 0,$$

where k ranges from 1 to n, and, for each k, r takes on all values from 1 to n except k.

Corresponding to any multiple series, $\sum u_{[i]}$, converging restrictedly to zero and having bounded partial sums, we obtain from (40) (I), by allowing the m's to become infinite in the restricted manner, the identity

(47)
$$\left\{\sum_{i_1=0}^{\infty} \cdots \sum_{i_n=0}^{\infty}\right\} u_{[i]} f_{[i]}(\alpha) = \left\{\sum_{i_1=0}^{\infty} \cdots \sum_{i_n=0}^{\infty}\right\} s_{[i]} \Delta_{[1]} f_{[i]}(\alpha)$$
$$= \sum_{i_1=0}^{\infty} \cdots \sum_{i_n=0}^{\infty} s_{[i]} \Delta_{[1]} f_{[i]}(\alpha),$$

provided the convergence factors, $f_{[i]}(\alpha)$, satisfy the conditions of Theorem VII (I).

We wish to show that if the $s_{[i]}$ in (47) form a bounded sequence for which

$$\{\lim_{i_1,\cdots,i_n\to\infty}\} s_{[i]} = 0,$$

and the convergence factors, $f_{[i]}(\alpha)$, satisfy the various conditions $(F_k^{(r)})$, in addition to the requirements of Theorem VIII (I), the right hand member of (47) will tend to zero as α approaches α_0.

Corresponding to a given positive ϵ we can, in view of the various conditions $(F_k^{(r)})$, choose a θ such that we have $n(n-1)$ inequalities of the type

(48)
$$\varlimsup_{\alpha\to\alpha_0} \sum_{i_2=0}^{\infty} \cdots \sum_{i_n=0}^{\infty} \sum_{i_1=0}^{[\theta i_2]} |\Delta_{[1]} f_{[i]}(\alpha)| < \frac{\epsilon}{4n(n-1)C},$$

where the C is defined as in (37) (I). From these inequalities it follows that we may choose a set $E_1(\alpha)$, included in the set $E'(\alpha)$ of condition $(A_1)_n$ of 1.16, such that we have $n(n-1)$ inequalities of the type

(49)
$$\sum_{i_2=0}^{\infty} \cdots \sum_{i_n=0}^{\infty} \sum_{i_1=0}^{[\theta i_2]} |\Delta_{[1]} f_{[i]}(\alpha)| < \frac{\epsilon}{3n(n-1)C} \qquad\qquad E_1(\alpha).$$

Because of the restricted convergence of $s_{[i]}$ to zero we can choose $m_1, m_2, \cdots, m_n$, such that

(50)
$$|s_{[i]}| < \frac{\epsilon}{3K}$$
$$[i_1 > m_1, \cdots, i_n > m_n; \theta i_k < \theta i_j < \theta^{-1} i_k \quad (k \neq j, k, j = 1, 2, \cdots, n)],$$

where the K is defined as in condition $(A_1)_n$ of 1.16.

We next introduce some further notations. We shall represent by $M(i_2, i_3 \cdot \cdots, i_n; \theta)$ the maximum value among the $(n-1)$ integers, $[\theta i_2], [\theta i_3], \cdots, [\theta i_n]$, with similar designations for other combinations of the i's. We then define the following ranges of the indices $i_1, i_2, \cdots, i_n$:

(S_1) $i_2 \geq 0, i_3 \geq 0, \cdots, i_n \geq 0;$ $0 \leq i_1 \leq M(i_2, i_3, \cdots, i_n; \theta),$

(S_2) $i_1 \geq 0, i_3 \geq 0, \cdots, i_n \geq 0;$ $0 \leq i_2 \leq M(i_1, i_3, \cdots, i_n; \theta),$

$\cdots\cdots\cdots\cdots\cdots\cdots\cdots\cdots\cdots\cdots\cdots\cdots\cdots\cdots\cdots$

(S_n) $i_1 \geq 0, i_2 \geq 0, \cdots, i_{n-1} \geq 0;$ $0 \leq i_n \leq M(i_1, i_2, \cdots, i_{n-1}; \theta).$

We further define (S_2') to include all sets of values of the indices in (S_2) not already found in (S_1), (S_3') to include all sets in (S_3) not found in (S_1) or (S_2'), and so on. Thus (S_n') will include all sets of values of the indices in (S_n), not already occurring in (S_1), (S_2'), $\cdots$, (S_{n-1}').

We also define two further ranges of the indices as follows:

$(S^{(1)})$ $\qquad \theta i_k < i_j < \theta^{-1} i_k$ $\hfill (k \neq j; k, j = 1, 2, \cdots, n)$

$\qquad\qquad\qquad$ and at least one of the inequalities $0 < i_k \leqq m_k$ holds,

$(S^{(2)})$ $\qquad \theta i_k < i_j < \theta^{-1} i_k \qquad i_k > m_k,$ $\qquad (k \neq j; k, j = 1, 2, \cdots, n).$

We note that the ranges $(S^{(1)})$, $(S^{(2)})$, (S_1), (S_2'), $\cdots$, (S_n') include all sets of values of the i's in $(i_1 \geqq 0, i_2 \geqq 0, \cdots, i_n \geqq 0)$, without duplication. Therefore the summation in the right hand member of (47) may be divided into $(n + 2)$ parts, corresponding to these ranges.

In view of the inequalities of type (49) we have for the portion of the summation in the right hand member of (47), extending over (S_1)

$$\left| \sum_{(S_1)} s_{[i]} \Delta_{[1]} f_{[i]}(\alpha) \right| \leqq C \sum_{(S_1)} | \Delta_{[1]} f_{[i]}(\alpha) |$$

$$(51) \qquad < C \sum_{i_2=0}^{\infty} \sum_{i_3=0}^{\infty} \cdots \sum_{i_n=0}^{\infty} \left(\sum_{i_1=0}^{[\theta i_2]} + \sum_{i_1=0}^{[\theta i_3]} + \cdots + \sum_{i_1=0}^{[\theta i_n]} \right) | \Delta_{[1]} f_{[i]}(\alpha) |$$

$$< \frac{\epsilon}{3n} \hfill E_1(\alpha).$$

We obtain similar inequalities for the summations over (S_2'), (S_3'), $\cdots$, (S_n').

From (50) and condition $(A_1)_n$ of Theorem VIII (I), we have

$$(52) \qquad \left| \sum_{(S^{(2)})} s_{[i]} \Delta_{[1]} f_{[i]}(\alpha) \right| < \frac{\epsilon}{3} \hfill E'(\alpha).$$

It follows from the various conditions (E_s) of Theorem VIII (I) that we can choose a set $E_2(\alpha)$, included in $E_1(\alpha)$ and therefore in $E'(\alpha)$, such that

$$(53) \qquad \left| \sum_{(S^{(1)})} s_{[i]} \Delta_{[1]} f_{[i]}(\alpha) \right| < \frac{\epsilon}{3} \hfill E_2(\alpha).$$

Combining (52), (53), and the n inequalities of type (51), we have

$$(54) \qquad \left| \left\{ \sum_{i_1=0}^{\infty} \cdots \sum_{i_n=0}^{\infty} \right\} u_{[i]} f_{[i]}(\alpha) \right| = \left| \sum_{i_1=0}^{\infty} \cdots \sum_{i_n=0}^{\infty} s_{[i]} \Delta_{[1]} f_{[i]}(\alpha) \right| < \epsilon \qquad E_2(\alpha),$$

and therefore the conditions of Theorem VIII (I), with the various supplementary conditions $(F_k^{(r)})$, are sufficient for convergence factors of type II in the case of multiple series converging restrictedly to zero. Since any restrictedly convergent multiple series reduces to this case by alteration of $u_{[0]}$, the sufficiency of the conditions is proved in general.

6.9. **Necessity of the conditions.** The conditions of Theorem VIII (I) were proved necessary for convergence factors of type II in 1.14 and 1.17. The multiple series involved in these proofs are all restrictedly convergent, and hence the proofs also establish the necessity of these same conditions when we confine ourselves to the class of restrictedly convergent multiple series. It remains to prove the necessity of the various supplementary conditions $(F_k^{(r)})$.

The proofs for the $n(n-1)$ individual cases are entirely analogous, so we shall confine ourselves to the case of condition $(F_1^{(2)})$. Since, moreover, the proof follows the same general procedure as the proof of the necessity of (F_1) of Theorem I in 6.4, we shall give it in somewhat less detail.

We begin by determining a positive ϵ such that

$$(55) \qquad \sum_{i_2=0}^{\infty} \cdots \sum_{i_n=0}^{\infty} \sum_{i_1=0}^{[\theta i_2]} |\Delta_{[1]} f_{[i]}(\alpha)| > 5\epsilon$$

for a set of values of θ $(\theta_1, \theta_2, \cdots, \theta_k, \cdots)$, tending to zero as a limit, and a corresponding set of values of α $(\alpha_1, \alpha_2, \cdots, \alpha_k, \cdots)$, tending to α_0 as a limit. Such a determination is of course possible in case $(F_1^{(2)})$ does not hold. We next select $\theta^{(1)}$ from the sequence of values of θ and let $\alpha^{(1)}$ represent the corresponding value of α. We then choose $m_2^{(1)}$ such that

$$(56) \qquad \sum_{i_2=0}^{m_2^{(1)}} \sum_{i_3=0}^{\infty} \cdots \sum_{i_n=0}^{\infty} \sum_{i_1=0}^{[\theta^{(1)} i_2]} |\Delta_{[1]} f_{[i]}(\alpha^{(1)})| > 4\epsilon,$$

and define

(57) $s_{[i]} = \operatorname{sgn} \Delta_{[1]} f_{[i]}(\alpha^{(1)})$ $(0 \le i_2 \le m_2^{(1)}, 0 \le i_3, \cdots, 0 \le i_n, 0 \le i_1 \le \theta^{(1)} i_2)$.

We further choose $p_2^{(1)} > m_2^{(1)}$ and such that

$$(58) \qquad \sum_{i_2=p_2^{(1)}}^{\infty} \sum_{i_3=0}^{\infty} \cdots \sum_{i_n=0}^{\infty} \sum_{i_1=0}^{[\theta^{(1)} i_2]} |\Delta_{[1]} f_{[i]}(\alpha^{(1)})| < \epsilon,$$

which can be done, in view of condition $(A)_n$ of Theorem VIII (I), already shown necessary. We now define

(59) $s_{[i]} = 0$ $(m_2^{(1)} < i_2 < p_2^{(1)}, 0 \le i_3, \cdots, 0 \le i_n, 0 \le i_1 \le \theta^{(1)} i_2)$,

and prescribe that all other $s_{[i]}$ whose indices lie in the range $(0 \le i_2, 0 \le i_3, \cdots, 0 \le i_n, 0 \le i_1 \le \theta^{(1)} j)$ shall have values whose absolute value is unity or zero, while all remaining $s_{[i]}$ are taken equal to zero. We then have from (56), (57), (58), and (59)

$$(60) \qquad \left| \sum_{i_1=0}^{\infty} \sum_{i_2=0}^{\infty} \cdots \sum_{i_n=0}^{\infty} s_{[i]} \Delta_{[1]} f_{[i]}(\alpha^{(1)}) \right| > 3\epsilon.$$

We next choose from the α_k a value $\alpha^{(2)}$ beyond $\alpha^{(1)}$ and such that

$$(61) \qquad \sum_{i_2=0}^{m_2^{(1)}} \sum_{i_3=0}^{\infty} \cdots \sum_{i_n=0}^{\infty} \sum_{i_1=0}^{[\theta^{(1)} i_2]} |\Delta_{[1]} f_{[i]}(\alpha^{(2)})| < \frac{\epsilon}{2},$$

which may be done, in view of condition $(E_2)_n$ of Theorem VIII (I), already proved necessary.   We also choose $q_2^{(1)} > p_2^{(1)}$ and such that

$$(62) \qquad \sum_{i_2=q_2^{(1)}}^{\infty} \sum_{i_3=0}^{\infty} \cdots \sum_{i_n=0}^{\infty} \sum_{i_1=0}^{[\theta^{(1)}i_2]} |\, \Delta_{[1]} f_{[i]}(\alpha^{(2)})\,| < \frac{\epsilon}{2}.$$

Then we set

$$(63) \qquad s_{[i]} = 0 \qquad (p_2^{(1)} \leqq i_2 \leqq q_2^{(1)}, 0 \leqq i_3 , \cdots , 0 \leqq i_n , 0 \leqq i_1 \leqq \theta^{(1)} i_2),$$

it being further presupposed that the remaining s's not yet explicitly defined have absolute values that do not exceed unity.   We thus have from (61) and (62)

$$(64) \qquad \left| \sum_{i_1=0}^{\infty} \sum_{i_2=0}^{\infty} \cdots \sum_{i_n=0}^{\infty} s_{[i]} \Delta_{[1]} f_{[i]}(\alpha^{(2)}) \right| < \epsilon.$$

We continue the procedure of choosing the α's, θ's, and s's in a manner analogous to that adopted in the case of double series in 6.4.   It is apparent that the i_2 and i_1 in the present case play the same rôle as the j and i in the previous case, and that conditions $(A)_n$ and $(E_2)_n$ serve the same purpose now as conditions $(A)_2$ and (C_2) in the discussion of double series.   We thus define a multiple series, with bounded partial sums, converging restrictedly to zero, for which the right hand side of (47) oscillates between values greater in absolute value than 2ϵ and less in absolute value than ϵ as α takes on the values $\alpha^{(1)}, \alpha^{(2)}, \alpha^{(3)}, \cdots ,$ tending to α_0.   This contradiction establishes the necessity of condition $(F_1^{(2)})$, and as stated before the proof of the necessity of any of the other supplementary conditions $(F_k^{(r)})$ is entirely analogous.

We have thus established the following theorem:

THEOREM III.   *The necessary and sufficient conditions that the series $\sum u_{[i]} f_{[i]}(\alpha)$ shall be restrictedly convergent in $E(\alpha)$ whenever the series $\sum u_{[i]}$ has this property, and that the value of the former series shall approach that of the latter series as α approaches α_0, are that the convergence factors, $f_{[i]}(\alpha)$, should satisfy the conditions of Theorem VIII (I) and the various supplementary conditions $(F_k^{(r)})$.*

6.10. **Sequence to function transformations for multiple sequences.**   We pointed out in 6.7 that the condition $(A^*)_n$ was necessary and sufficient for the convergence in $E(\alpha)$ of $\sum s_{[i]} \varphi_{[i]}(\alpha)$, whenever $s_{[i]}$ is bounded and restrictedly convergent.   To find the necessary and sufficient conditions that $\sum s_{[i]} \varphi_{[i]}(\alpha)$ shall also approach the value to which $s_{[i]}$ converges as α approaches α_0, we apply Theorem III to the related series with convergence factors, $\sum u_{[i]} f_{[i]}(\alpha)$, where $f_{[i]}(\alpha)$ is defined in terms of the $\varphi_{[i]}(\alpha)$ by means of (50) (I), and then transform the conditions of Theorem III into conditions involving the $\varphi_{[i]}(\alpha)$ by means of the relations (51) (I).   We thus obtain the following theorem:

THEOREM IV.   *The necessary and sufficient conditions that for every bounded and restrictedly convergent multiple sequence $(s_{[i]})$ the series $\sum s_{[i]} \varphi_{[i]}(\alpha)$ shall converge in $E(\alpha)$ and shall approach the value to which the multiple sequence converges in the* *restricted manner as α approaches α_0, are that the functions $\varphi_{[i]}(\alpha)$ satisfy the conditions of Theorem IX (I) and the various supplementary conditions $(F_k^{(r)}*)$ of type*

$(F_1^{(2)}*)$ $$\varlimsup_{\alpha \to \alpha_0} \sum_{i_2=0}^{\infty} \cdots \sum_{i_n=0}^{\infty} \sum_{i_1=0}^{[\theta i_2]} |\varphi_{[i]}(\alpha)| \to 0 \text{ as } \theta \to 0.$$

As applications of Theorem IV, we readily obtain special cases of this theorem analogous to the special cases of Theorem II, discussed in 6.5.

BIBLIOGRAPHY

The bibliography includes all literature referred to in the text and other closely related work. References to the bibliography are indicated by numbers in square brackets.

ABEL, N. H.
1. *Untersuchungen über die Reihe u. s. w.* Journal für die Reine und Angewandte Mathematik, gegründet von A. L. Crelle 1826, vol. 2 (1827), p. 286. Ostwald's Klassiker, No. 71. Leipzig, Engelman, 1895. Trad. française: *Oeuvres complètes*, new ed., vol. 1, 1881, pp. 219-250.

ADAMS, C. R.
2. *On multiple factorial series.* Annals of Mathematics, (2), vol. 32 (1931), pp. 67-82.
3. *Transformations of double sequences with applications to Cesàro summability of double series.* Bulletin of the American Mathematical Society, vol. 37 (1931), pp. 741-748.
4. *On summability of double series.* Transactions of the American Mathematical Society, vol. 34 (1932), pp. 215-230.
5. *Note on multiple Dirichlet and multiple factorial series.* Annals of Mathematics, (2), vol. 33 (1932), pp. 406-412.
6. *On non-factorable transformations of double sequences.* Proceedings of the National Academy of Sciences, vol. 19 (1933), pp. 564-567.
7. *Hausdorff transformations for double sequences.* Bulletin of the American Mathematical Society, vol. 39 (1933), pp. 303-312.

AGNEW, R. P.
8. *On summability of double sequences.* American Journal of Mathematics, vol. 54 (1932), pp. 648-656.
9. *On equivalence of methods of evaluation of sequences.* The Tôhoku Mathematical Journal, vol. 35 (1932), pp. 244-252.
10. *On summability of multiple sequences.* American Journal of Mathematics, vol. 56 (1934), pp. 62-68.

ANDERSEN, A. F.
11. *Studier over Cesàro's Summabilitetsmetode. Med saerlig anvendelse overfor potensraekkernes theori.* Dissertation, Copenhagen, 1921.

BERNOULLI, D.
12. *De summationibus serierum quarundam incongrue veris earumque interpretatione atque usu.* Novi Commentarii Academiae Scientiarum Petropolitanae, vol. 16 (1771), 1772, pp. 71-90, summary pp. 12-15.

BÔCHER, M.
13. *Introduction to the theory of Fourier's series.* Annals of Mathematics, (2), vol. 7 (1905-06), pp. 81-152.

BOCHNER, S.
14. *Die Poissonsche Summationsformel in mehrerem Veränderlichen.* Mathematische Annalen, vol. 106 (1932), pp. 56-63.
15a. *Limitierung mehrfacher Folgen nach dem Verfahren der arithmetischen Mittel.* Mathematische Zeitschrift, vol. 35 (1932), pp. 122-126.
15b. *Summation of multiple Fourier series by spherical means.* Transactions of the American Mathematical Society, vol. 40 (1936), pp. 175-207.

BOHR, H.
16. *Sur la série de Dirichlet.* Comptes Rendus Hebdomadaires des Séances de l'Académie des Sciences, Paris, vol. 148 (1909), pp. 75-80.
17. *Bidrag til de Dirichlet'ske Raekkers Theori. Contribution à la théorie des séries de Dirichlet.* Dissertation, Copenhagen, 1910.

BOREL, É.
18. *Fondements de la théorie des séries divergentes sommables.* Journal de Mathématiques Pures et Appliquées, Liouville, (5), vol. 2 (1896), pp. 103–122.
19. *Mémoire sur les séries divergentes.* Annales Scientifiques de l'École Normale Supérieure, Paris, (3), vol. 16 (1899), pp. 9–131, 132–136.
20. *Leçons sur les Séries Divergentes.* Chaps. III–V. Paris, Gauthier-Villars, 1901.

BOREL, É., and BOULIGAND, G.
21. *Leçons sur les Séries Divergentes.* 2d. ed., Chaps. III–VI. Paris, Gauthier-Villars, 1928.

BOULIGAND, G.
See Borel, É., and Bouligand, G.

BROMWICH, T. J. I'A.
22. *On the limits of certain infinite series and integrals.* Mathematische Annalen, vol. 65 (1908), pp. 350–369.
23. *Various extensions of Abel's lemma.* Proceedings of the London Mathematical Society, (2), vol. 6 (1907), pp. 58–76.
24. *An Introduction to the Theory of Infinite Series.* Chap. XI. London, Macmillan, 1908.

BROMWICH, T. J. I'A., and HARDY, G. H.
25. *Some extensions to multiple series of Abel's theorem on the continuity of power series.* Proceedings of the London Mathematical Society, (2), vol. 2 (1904), pp. 161–189.

BURKHARDT, H.
26. *Über den Gebrauch divergenter Reihen in der Zeit von 1750–1850.* Mathematische Annalen, vol. 70 (1911), pp. 169–206.

CARLSON, F.
27. *Une remarque sur la transformation de séries sommables en séries convergentes.* Nyt Tidsskrift for Matematik, vol. 28 (1917), pp. 81–88.

CARMICHAEL, R. D.
28. *Note on convergence tests applicable to series converging conditionally.* The Tôhoku Mathematical Journal, vol. 11 (1917), pp. 191–199.
29. *General aspects of the theory of summable series.* Bulletin of the American Mathematical Society, vol. 25 (1918), pp. 97–131.

CESÀRO, E.
30. *Sur la multiplication des séries.* Bulletin des Sciences Mathématiques, Darboux, (2), vol. 14 (1890), pp. 114–120.

CHAPMAN, S.
31. *On non-integral orders of summability of series and integrals.* Proceedings of the London Mathematical Society, (2), vol. 9 (1910), pp. 369–409.
See also Hardy, G. H., and Chapman, S.

DIENES, P.
32. *The Taylor Series.* Oxford, Clarendon Press, 1931.

DURFEE, W. H.
33. *Summation factors which are powers of a complex variable.* American Journal of Mathematics, vol. 53 (1931), pp. 817–842.
34. *Convergence factors for double series.* Bulletin of the American Mathematical Society, vol. 39 (1933), pp. 457–464.

EULER, L.
35. *De seriebus divergentibus.* Novi Commentarii Academiae Scientiarum Petropolitanae, vol. 5 (1754–55), 1760, pp. 205–237; summarium ibidem, pp. 19–23. Also in *Leonhardi Euleri Opera Omnia*, series prima, vol. 14 (1924), pp. 585–617.
36. *Observationes generales circe series, quarum termini secundum sinus vel cosinus angulorum multiplorum progrediuntur.* Nova Acta Academiae Scientiarum Petropolitanae, vol. 7 (1789), 1793, pp. 87–98; summarium ibidem, pp. 41–42.
37. *Leonhardi Euleri Opera Omnia.* Series prima, vol. 16 (1933), pp. 163–177.

EVERSULL, B. M.

    38. *On convergence factors in triple series and the triple Fourier's series.* Annals of
        Mathematics, (2), vol. 24 (1922-23), pp. 141-166.

    39. *The summability of the triple Fourier series at points of discontinuity of the function
        developed.* Transactions of the American Mathematical Society, vol. 26 (1924),
        pp. 313-334.

FEJÉR, L.

    40. *Sur les fonctions bornées et intégrables.* Comptes Rendus Hebdomadaires des
        Séances de l'Académie des Sciences, Paris, vol. 131 (1900), pp. 984-987.

    41. *Untersuchungen aus dem Gebiete der Fourierschen Reihen.* Mathematikai és
        Physikai Lapok, vol. 10 (1902), pp. 49-68, 97-123.

    42. *Untersuchungen über Fouriersche Reihen.* Mathematische Annalen, vol. 58 (1903),
        pp. 51-69.

FEKETE, M.

    43. *Summabilitási factorsorozatok.* Mathematikai és Természettudományi Értesitö,
        vol. 35 (1917), pp. 309-324.

FORD, W. B.

    44. *On the relation between the sum-formulas of Hölder and Cesàro.* American Journal
        of Mathematics, vol. 32 (1910), pp. 315-326.

    45. *Studies on Divergent Series and Summability.* University of Michigan Science
        Series, vol. 2. New York, Macmillan, 1916.

FORT, T.

    46. *Infinite Series.* Chap. XVII. Oxford, Clarendon Press, 1930.

FRALEIGH, P. A.

    47. *Regular bilinear transformation of sequences.* American Journal of Mathematics,
        vol. 53 (1931), pp. 697-709.

FROBENIUS, G.

    48. *Über die Leibnitzsche Reihe.* Journal für die Reine und Angewandte Mathematik
        (Crelle), vol. 89 (1880), pp. 262-264.

GARABEDIAN, H. L.

    49. *On the relation between certain methods of summability.* Annals of Mathematics,
        (2), vol. 32 (1931), pp. 83-106.

    50. *A convergence factor theorem in the theory of summable series.* Bulletin of the
        American Mathematical Society, vol. 41 (1935), pp. 583-592.

GIBSON, G. A.

    51. *An extension of Abel's theorem on the continuity of a power series.* Proceedings of
        the Edinburgh Mathematical Society, vol. 19 (1901), pp. 67-70.

GILMAN, R. E.

    52. *A remark on Nörlund's method of summation.* Annals of Mathematics, (2), vol. 33
        (1932), pp. 429-432.

GRISAR, C. G.

    53. *Über eine Verallgemeinerung des Tauberschen Satzes und seine Ausdehnung auf
        n-fache Reihen.* Dissertation, Munich, 1924.

GRONWALL, T. H.

    54. *Summation of series and conformal mapping.* Annals of Mathematics, (2), vol. 33
        (1932), pp. 101-117.

GROSZ, W.

    55. *Zur Poissonschen Summierung.* Sitzungsberichte der Mathematisch-Natur-
        wissenschaftlichen Klasse der Kaiserlichen Akademie der Wissenschaften zu
        Wien, vol. 124 (1915), pp. 1017-1037.

HADAMARD, J.

    56. *Deux théorèmes d'Abel sur la convergence des séries.* Acta Mathematica, vol. 27
        (1903), pp. 177-183.

HAHN, H.
57. *Über Reihen mit monoton abnehmenden Gliedern.* Monatshefte für Mathematik und Physik, vol. 33 (1923), pp. 121–134.

HALLENBACH, F.
58. *Zur Theorie der Limitierungsverfahren von Doppelfolgen.* Dissertation, Bonn, 1933.

HAMILTON, H. J.
59. *On transformations of double series.* Bulletin of the American Mathematical Society, vol. 42 (1936), pp. 275–283.
60. *Transformations of multiple sequences.* Duke Mathematical Journal, vol. 2 (1936), pp. 29–60.

HARDY, G. H.
61. *Researches in the theory of divergent series and divergent integrals.* The Quarterly Journal of Pure and Applied Mathematics, vol. 35 (1903), pp. 22–66.
62. *Some theorems connected with Abel's theorem on the continuity of power series.* Proceedings of the London Mathematical Society, (2), vol. 4 (1906), pp. 247–265.
63. *Some theorems concerning infinite series.* Mathematische Annalen, vol. 64 (1907), pp. 77–94.
64. *Generalization of a theorem in the theory of divergent series.* Proceedings of the London Mathematical Society, (2), vol. 6 (1907), pp. 255–264.
65. *Theorems relating to the summability and convergence of slowly oscillating series.* Proceedings of the London Mathematical Society, (2), vol. 8 (1909), pp. 301–320.
66. *On the convergence of certain multiple series.* Proceedings of the Cambridge Philosophical Society, vol. 19 (1920), pp. 86–95.
See also Bromwich, T. J. I'A, and Hardy, G. H.

HARDY, G. H., and CHAPMAN, S.
67. *A general view of the theory of summable series.* The Quarterly Journal of Pure and Applied Mathematics, vol. 42 (1911), pp. 181–215.

HARDY, G. H., and LITTLEWOOD, J. E.
68. *Contributions to the arithmetic theory of series.* Proceedings of the London Mathematical Society, (2), vol. 11 (1912), pp. 411–478.

HARDY, G. H., and RIESZ, M.
69. *The General Theory of Dirichlet's Series.* Cambridge Mathematical Tracts, No. 18, 1915.

HAUSDORFF, F.
70. *Summationsmethoden und Momentfolgen.* I and II. Mathematische Zeitschrift, vol. 9 (1921), pp. 74–109, 280–299.

HILL, J. D.
71. *A theorem in the theory of summability.* Bulletin of the American Mathematical Society, vol. 42 (1936), pp. 225–228.

HILLE, E.
72. *Essai d'une bibliographie de la représentation analytique d'une fonction monogène.* Acta Mathematica, vol. 52 (1929), pp. 1–80.
73. *Summation of Fourier series.* Bulletin of the American Mathematical Society, vol. 38 (1932), pp. 505–528.

HILLE, E., and TAMARKIN, J. D.
74. *On the summability of Fourier series.* Proceedings of the National Academy of Sciences, vol. 14 (1928), pp. 915–918.
75. *On the summability of Fourier series.* I. Transactions of the American Mathematical Society, vol. 34 (1932), pp. 757–783.
76. *On the summability of Fourier series.* III. Mathematische Annalen, vol. 108 (1933), pp. 525–577.

HÖLDER, O.
 77. *Grenzwerthe von Reihen an der Convergenzgrenze.* Mathematische Annalen, vol. 20 (1882), pp. 535-549.
HOLZBERGER, H.
 78. *Über das Verhalten von Potenzreihen mit zwei und drei Veränderlichen an der Konvergenzgrenze.* Monatshefte für Mathematik und Physik, vol. 25 (1914), pp. 179-266. Also dissertation, Munich, 1913.
HURWITZ, W. A.
 79. *Convergence-factors in Cesàro-summable series.* Abstract, Bulletin of the American Mathematical Society, vol. 28 (1922), p. 156.
 80. *Report on topics in the theory of divergent series.* Bulletin of the American Mathematical Society, vol. 28 (1922), pp. 17-36.
HURWITZ, W. A., and SILVERMAN, L. L.
 81. *On the consistency and equivalence of certain definitions of summability.* Transactions of the American Mathematical Society, vol. 18 (1917), pp. 1-20.
IZUMI, S.
 82. *Über die lineare Transformation in der Theorie der unendlichen Reihen.* The Tôhoku Mathematical Journal, vol. 27 (1926), pp. 313-323.
JACOBSTHAL, E.
 83. *Mittelwertbildung und Reihentransformation.* Mathematische Zeitschrift, vol. 6 (1920), pp. 100-117.
JAMES, G.
 84. *Some theorems on the summation of divergent series.* Dissertation, Columbia, 1917.
 85. *On the theory of summability.* Annals of Mathematics, (2), vol. 21 (1919), pp. 120-127.
JULIA, G.
 86. *À propos du théorème d'Abel sur les séries entières.* Bulletin des Sciences Mathématiques, Darboux, (2), vol. 55 (1931), pp. 35-41.
KIENAST, A.
 87. *Extensions of Abel's theorem and its converses.* Proceedings of the Cambridge Philosophical Society, vol. 19 (1918), pp. 129-147.
KNOPP, K.
 88. *Grenzwerte von Reihen bei der Annäherung an die Konvergenzgrenze.* Dissertation, Berlin, 1907.
 89. *Mittelwertbildung und Reihen Transformation.* Mathematische Zeitschrift, vol. 6 (1920), pp. 118-123.
 90. *Neuere Untersuchungen in der Theorie der divergenten Reihen.* Jahresbericht der Deutschen Mathematiker-Vereinigung, vol. 32 (1923), pp. 43-67.
 91. *Zur Theorie der Limitierungsverfahren.* I and II. Mathematische Zeitschrift, vol. 31 (1929-30), pp. 97-127, 276-305.
 92. *Theorie und Anwendung der unendlichen Reihen.* Chap. XIII. Berlin, Springer, 1922. 2d. ed., 1924. English translation of 2d. ed. by Mrs. R. C. Young, 1928. 3d. ed., 1931.
KOGBETLIANTZ, E.
 93. *Sommation des séries et intégrales divergentes par les moyennes arithmétiques et typiques.* Mémorial des Sciences Mathématiques, No. 51. Paris, Gauthier-Villars, 1931.
KOJIMA, T.
 94. *On generalized Toeplitz's theorems on limit and their applications.* The Tôhoku Mathematical Journal, vol. 12 (1917), pp. 291-326.
 95. *Theorems on double series.* The Tôhoku Mathematical Journal, vol. 17 (1920), pp. 213-220.

96. *On the theory of double sequences.* The Tôhoku Mathematical Journal, vol. 21 (1922), pp. 3–14.

LAGRANGE, J. L.

97. *Rapport sur un mémoire présenté à la classe par le citoyen Callet.* (Signed: Bossut, Lagrange, commissaires.) Mémoires de l'Institut National des Sciences et Arts, Sciences Mathématiques et Physiques, vol. 3 (1799).

LANDAU, E.

98. *Darstellung und Begrundung einiger neuerer Ergebnisse der Funktionentheorie.* Chap. II. Berlin, Springer, 1916.

LEIBNIZ, G.

99. *Extract from a letter to Boyle.* Nouvelles de la République des Lettres, edited by P. Boyle, Amsterdam, vol. 8 (1687), pp. 744–753.

100. *Epistola ad V. I. Christianum Wolfium, professorem Matheseos Halensem circa scientiam infiniti.* Acta Eruditorum, Supplementum, vol. 5 (1713), pp. 264–270.

LEIBNIZ, G., and WOLF, C.

101. *Briefwechsel zwischen Leibniz und Christian Wolf.* Handschriften der Koeniglichen Bibliothek zu Hannover, herausgegeben von C. I. Gerhardt, Halle, 1860. Letters LXX, LXXI, pp. 143–148.

LEJA, M. F.

102. *Sur la continuité de la somme des séries entières multiples.* Bulletin de la Société Mathématique de France, vol. 57 (1929), pp. 72–77.

LENSE, J.

103. *Über lineare Transformationen von Zahlenfolgen.* Mathematische Zeitschrift, vol. 36 (1932), pp. 99–103.

LE ROY, E.

104. *Sur les séries divergentes.* Comptes Rendus Hebdomadaires des Séances de l'Académie des Sciences, Paris, vol. 130 (1900), pp. 1293–1296, 1535–1536.

105. *Sur les séries divergentes et les fonctions définies par un développement de Taylor.* Annales de la Faculté des Sciences de Toulouse pour les Sciences Mathématiques et les Sciences Physiques, (2), vol. 2 (1900), pp. 317–430.

LÉVY, P.

106. *Sur les conditions d'application et sur la régularité des procédés de sommation des séries divergentes.* Bulletin de la Société Mathématique de France, vol. 54 (1926), pp. 1–25.

LITTLEWOOD, J. E.

See Hardy, G. H., and Littlewood, J. E.

LÖSCH, F.

107. *Über den Permanenzsatz gewisser Limitierungsverfahren für Doppelfolgen.* Mathematische Zeitschrift, vol. 34 (1931), pp. 281–290.

108. *Über den Permanenzsatz gewisser Limitierungsverfahren für Doppelfolgen.* II. Mathematische Zeitschrift, vol. 37 (1933), pp. 77–84.

109. *Über restringierte Limitierung von Doppelfolgen.* Mathematische Annalen, vol. 110 (1934), pp. 33–53.

MAZURKIEWICZ, ST.

110. *O sumowalnosci szeregów ksztoltu (Summability of the series $\sum a_n u_n$).* Sitzungsberichte der Warschauen Gesellschaft der Wissenschaften, vol. 8 (1915), pp. 649–655.

MEARS, F. M.

111. *Some multiplication theorems for the Nörlund mean.* Bulletin of the American Mathematical Society, vol. 41 (1935), pp. 875–880.

MILLER, H. L., and ODOMS, A. H.

112. *On the summability of multiple Fourier series.* The Tôhoku Mathematical Journal, vol. 42 (1936), pp. 155–175.

MOORE, C. N.

113. *On the introduction of convergence factors into summable series and summable integrals.* Transactions of the American Mathematical Society, vol. 8 (1907), pp. 299–330.

114. *Summability of the developments in Bessel's functions, with applications.* Transactions of the American Mathematical Society, vol. 10 (1909), pp. 391–435.

115. *Sur les facteurs de convergence dans les séries doubles et sur la série double de Fourier.* Comptes Rendus Hebdomadaires des Séances de l'Académies de Sciences, Paris, vol. 155 (1912), pp. 126–129.

116. *On convergence factors in double series and the double Fourier's series.* Transactions of the American Mathematical Society, vol. 14 (1913), pp. 73–104.

117. *On the summability of the double Fourier's series of discontinuous functions.* Mathematische Annalen, vol. 74 (1913), pp. 555–572.

118. *Sur la rélation entre certaines méthodes pour la sommation d'une série divergente.* Comptes Rendus Hebdomadaires des Séances de l'Académie des Sciences, Paris, vol. 158 (1914), pp. 1774–1775.

119. *Applications of the theory of summability to developments in orthogonal functions.* Bulletin of the American Mathematical Society, vol. 25 (1919), pp. 258–276.

120. *On convergence factors in multiple series.* Abstract, Bulletin of the American Mathematical Society, vol. 32 (1926), pp. 16–17.

121. *On convergence factors in multiple series.* Transactions of the American Mathematical Society, vol. 29 (1927), pp. 227–238.

122. *On convergence factors for double series that are summable of non-integral orders.* Abstract, Bulletin of the American Mathematical Society, vol. 40 (1934), pp. 32–33.

123. *On convergence factors for series summable by Nörlund means.* Proceedings of the National Academy of Sciences, vol. 21 (1935), pp. 263–266.

124. *Convergence factors for double series summable by Nörlund means.* Proceedings of the National Academy of Sciences, vol. 22 (1936), pp. 167–170.

MORSE, D. S.

125. *Relative inclusiveness of certain definitions of summability.* American Journal of Mathematics, vol. 45 (1923), pp. 259–285.

NÖRLUND, N. E.

126. *Sur une application des fonctions permutables.* Lunds Universitets Arsskrift, Avdelning 2, vol. 16, No. 3 (1919).

OBRECHKOFF, N.

127. *Sur la sommation des séries divergentes.* Acta Mathematica, vol. 63 (1934), pp. 1–75.

ODOMS, A. H.

See Miller, H. L., and Odoms, A. H.

OTTOLENGHI, B.

128. *Somma generalizzata e grado di indeterminazione delle serie.* Giornale di Matematiche di Battaglini, vol. 49 (1911), pp. 233–279.

PERRON, O.

129. *Beitrag zur Theorie der divergenten Reihen.* Mathematische Zeitschrift, vol. 6 (1920), pp. 286–310.

POISSON, S. D.

130. *Mémoire sur la manière d'exprimer les fonctions par des séries de quantités périodiques, et sur l'usage de cette transformation dans la résolution de différens problèmes.* Journal de l'École Polytechnique, vol. 11 (1820), pp. 417–489.

PRINGSHEIM, A.

131. *Über zwei Abel'sche Sätze, die Stetigkeit von Reihensummen betreffend.* Sitzungsberichte der Mathematisch-Physikalischen Klasse der Königlichen Bayerischen Akademie der Wissenschaften zu München, vol. 27 (1897), pp. 343–356.

RAABE, J. L.
132. *Über die Summation periodischer Reihen und die Reduction des Integrals* $\int_0^\infty \varphi$ (sin *ax* cos *bx*)*dx*. Journal für die Reine und Angewandte Mathematik (Crelle), vol. 15 (1836), pp. 355–364.

RAFF, H.
133. *Beschränkte divergente Folgen und reguläre Matrizen.* Mathematische Zeitschrift, vol. 36 (1932), pp. 1–34.

REIFF, R.
134. *Geschichte der Unendlichen Reihen.* Tübingen, 1889.

REY PASTOR, J.
135. *Teoría de los algoritmos lineales de convergencia y de sumación.* Publicaciones, Serie B, Facultad de Ciencias Exactas, Fisicas y Naturales, University of Buenos Aires, No. 12 (1932), pp. 51–222.

RIESZ, M.
136. *Sur les séries de Dirichlet.* Comptes Rendus Hebdomadaires des Séances de l'Académie des Sciences, Paris, vol. 148 (1909), pp. 1658–1660.
137. *Une méthode de sommation équivalente à la méthode des moyennes arithmétiques.* Comptes Rendus Hebdomadaires des Séances de l'Académie des Sciences, Paris, vol. 152 (1911), pp. 1651–1654.
138. *Sur l'équivalence de certaines méthodes de sommation.* Proceedings of the London Mathematical Society, (2), vol. 22 (1924), pp. 412–419.
See also Hardy, G. H., and Riesz, M.

ROBISON, G. M.
139. *Divergent double sequences and series.* Transactions of the American Mathematical Society, vol. 28 (1926), pp. 50–73.

ROGOSINSKI, W.
140. *Reihensummierung durch Abschnittskoppelungen.* I. Mathematische Zeitschrift, vol. 25 (1926), pp. 132–149.

SANNIA, G.
141. *Nuovo metodo di sommazione delle serie: estensione del metodo di Borel.* Rendiconti del Circolo Matematico di Palermo, vol. 42 (1917), pp. 303–322.

SCHMIDT, R.
142. *Über divergente Folgen und lineare Mittelbildungen.* Mathematische Zeitschrift, vol. 22 (1925), pp. 89–152.

SCHNEE, W.
143. *Die Identität des Cesàroschen und Hölderschen Grenzwertes.* Mathematische Annalen, vol. 67 (1909), pp. 110–125.

SCHUR, I.
144. *Über die Äquivalenz der Cesàroschen und Hölderschen Mittelwerte.* Mathematische Annalen, vol. 74 (1913), pp. 447–458.
145. *Über lineare Transformationen in der Theorie der unendlichen Reihen.* Journal für die Reine und Angewandte Mathematik (Crelle), vol. 151 (1921), pp. 79–111.

SCHWARZ, H. A.
146. *Gesammelte Mathematische Abhandlungen.* Vol. 2, pp. 360–361. Berlin, 1890.

SILVERMAN, L. L.
147. *On the definition of the sum of a divergent series.* University of Missouri Studies, Mathematics Series, vol. 1, no. 1 (1913).
See also Hurwitz, W. A., and Silverman, L. L.

SILVERMAN, L. L., and TAMARKIN, J. D.
148. *On the generalization of Abel's theorem for certain definitions of summability.* Mathematische Zeitschrift, vol. 29 (1928), pp. 161–170.

SMAIL, L. L.
149. *Some generalizations in the theory of summable divergent series.* Dissertation, Columbia, 1913.

150. *Summability of double series.* Annals of Mathematics, (2), vol. 21 (1920), pp. 221-223.

151. *A theorem on convergence factors in summable series.* Bulletin of the American Mathematical Society, vol. 30 (1924), p. 197.

152. *History and synopsis of the theory of summable infinite processes.* University of Oregon Publications, 1925.

SZEGÖ, G.

153. *Ein Beispiel zu Nörlunds Summationsverfahren.* Annals of Mathematics, (2), vol. 34 (1933), pp. 379-380.

TAKENAKA, S.

154. *A general view of the theory of summability.* I. The Tôhoku Mathematical Journal, vol. 21 (1922), pp. 193-221.

155. *A general view of the theory of summability.* II. The Tôhoku Mathematical Journal, vol. 22 (1923), pp. 201-222.

TAMARKIN, J. D.

See Hille, E., and Tamarkin, J. D.; Silverman, L. L., and Tamarkin, J. D.; Woronoi and Tamarkin.

TOEPLITZ, O.

156. *Über allgemeine lineare Mittelbildungen.* Prace Matematyczno-fizyczne (Polish), vol. 22 (1911), pp. 113-119.

VAN VLECK, E. B.

157. *Selected topics in the theory of divergent series and continued fractions.* American Mathematical Society Colloquium Publications, vol. 1, Part III. New York, 1905.

WANG, F. T.

158. *On the convergence factor of Fourier-Lebesgue series.* Proceedings of the Imperial Academy of Japan, vol. 10 (1934), pp. 299-302.

159. *On the convergence factor of Fourier series at a point.* The Tôhoku Mathematical Journal, vol. 41 (1935), pp. 91-108.

WIENER, N.

160. *Tauberian theorems.* Annals of Mathematics, (2), vol. 33 (1932), pp. 1-100.

WOLF, C.

See Leibniz, G., and Wolf, C.

WORONOI, G. T.

161. *Extension of the notion of the limit of the sum of terms of an infinite series.* Proceedings (Dnevnik) of the XIth Congress (1901) of Russian Naturalists and Physicians, St. Petersburg, 1902, pp. 60-61.

WORONOI AND TAMARKIN

162. *Extension of the notion of the limit of the sum of terms of an infinite series.* Annals of Mathematics, (2), vol. 33 (1932), pp. 422-428. Translation of the previous note into English by J. D. Tamarkin, with supplementary remarks by the translator.

ZYGMUND, A.

163. *Sur une généralisation de la méthode de Cesàro.* Comptes Rendus Hebdomadaires des Séances de l'Académie des Sciences, Paris, vol. 179 (1924), pp. 870-872.

164. *O teorji srednich arythmetycznych.* Mathesis Polska, vol. 1 (1926), pp. 75-85, 119-129. (Cf. also a correction, ibid., vol. 5 (1930), p. 46.)

165. *Über einige Sätze aus der Theorie der divergenten Reihen.* Bulletin de l'Académie Polonaise, Série A, 1927, pp. 309-331.

INDEX

The numbers refer to pages

CATALOGUE OF DOVER BOOKS

MATHEMATICS—INTERMEDIATE TO ADVANCED

General

INTRODUCTION TO APPLIED MATHEMATICS, Francis D. Murnaghan. A practical and thoroughly sound introduction to a number of advanced branches of higher mathematics. Among the selected topics covered in detail are: vector and matrix analysis, partial and differential equations, integral equations, calculus of variations, Laplace transform theory, the vector triple product, linear vector functions, quadratic and bilinear forms, Fourier series, spherical harmonics, Bessel functions, the Heaviside expansion formula, and many others. Extremely useful book for graduate students in physics, engineering, chemistry, and mathematics. Index. 111 study exercises with answers. 41 illustrations. ix + 389pp. 5⅜ x 8½.
S1042 Paperbound **$2.00**

OPERATIONAL METHODS IN APPLIED MATHEMATICS, H. S. Carslaw and J. C. Jaeger. Explanation of the application of the Laplace Transformation to differential equations, a simple and effective substitute for more difficult and obscure operational methods. Of great practical value to engineers and to all workers in applied mathematics. Chapters on: Ordinary Linear Differential Equations with Constant Coefficients;; Electric Circuit Theory; Dynamical Applications; The Inversion Theorem for the Laplace Transformation; Conduction of Heat; Vibrations of Continuous Mechanical Systems; Hydrodynamics; Impulsive Functions; Chains of Differential Equations; and other related matters. 3 appendices. 153 problems, many with answers. 22 figures. xvi + 359pp. 5⅜ x 8½.
S1011 Paperbound **$2.25**

APPLIED MATHEMATICS FOR RADIO AND COMMUNICATIONS ENGINEERS, C. E. Smith. No extraneous material here!—only the theories, equations, and operations essential and immediately useful for radio work. Can be used as refresher, as handbook of applications and tables, or as full home-study course. Ranges from simplest arithmetic through calculus, series, and wave forms, hyperbolic trigonometry, simultaneous equations in mesh circuits, etc. Supplies applications right along with each math topic discussed. 22 useful tables of functions, formulas, logs, etc. Index. 166 exercises, 140 examples, all with answers. 95 diagrams. Bibliography. x + 336pp. 5⅜ x 8.
S141 Paperbound **$1.75**

Algebra, group theory, determinants, sets, matrix theory

ALGEBRAS AND THEIR ARITHMETICS, L. E. Dickson. Provides the foundation and background necessary to any advanced undergraduate or graduate student studying abstract algebra. Begins with elementary introduction to linear transformations, matrices, field of complex numbers; proceeds to order, basal units, modulus, quaternions, etc.; develops calculus of linears sets, describes various examples of algebras including invariant, difference, nilpotent, semi-simple. "Makes the reader marvel at his genius for clear and profound analysis," Amer. Mathematical Monthly. Index. xii + 241pp. 5⅜ x 8.
S616 Paperbound **$1.50**

THE THEORY OF EQUATIONS WITH AN INTRODUCTION TO THE THEORY OF BINARY ALGEBRAIC FORMS, W. S. Burnside and A. W. Panton. Extremely thorough and concrete discussion of the theory of equations, with extensive detailed treatment of many topics curtailed in later texts. Covers theory of algebraic equations, properties of polynomials, symmetric functions, derived functions, Horner's process, complex numbers and the complex variable, determinants and methods of elimination, invariant theory (nearly 100 pages), transformations, introduction to Galois theory, Abelian equations, and much more. Invaluable supplementary work for modern students and teachers. 759 examples and exercises. Index in each volume. Two volume set. Total of xxiv + 604pp. 5⅜ x 8.
S714 Vol I Paperbound **$1.85**
S715 Vol II Paperbound **$1.85**
The set **$3.70**

COMPUTATIONAL METHODS OF LINEAR ALGEBRA, V. N. Faddeeva, translated by **C. D. Benster.** First English translation of a unique and valuable work, the only work in English presenting a systematic exposition of the most important methods of linear algebra—classical and contemporary. Shows in detail how to derive numerical solutions of problems in mathematical physics which are frequently connected with those of linear algebra. Theory as well as individual practice. Part I surveys the mathematical background that is indispensable to what follows. Parts II and III, the conclusion, set forth the most important methods of solution, for both exact and iterative groups. One of the most outstanding and valuable features of this work is the 23 tables, double and triple checked for accuracy. These tables will not be found elsewhere. Author's preface. Translator's note. New bibliography and index. x + 252pp. 5⅜ x 8.
S424 Paperbound **$1.95**

ALGEBRAIC EQUATIONS, E. Dehn. Careful and complete presentation of Galois' theory of algebraic equations; theories of Lagrange and Galois developed in logical rather than historical form, with a more thorough exposition than in most modern books. Many concrete applications and fully-worked-out examples. Discusses basic theory (very clear exposition of the symmetric group); isomorphic, transitive, and Abelian groups; applications of Lagrange's and Galois' theories; and much more. Newly revised by the author. Index. List of Theorems. xi + 208pp. 5⅜ x 8.
S697 Paperbound **$1.45**

Catalogue of Dover Books

ALGEBRAIC THEORIES, L. E. Dickson. Best thorough introduction to classical topics in higher algebra develops theories centering around matrices, invariants, groups. Higher algebra, Galois theory, finite linear groups, Klein's icosahedron, algebraic invariants, linear transformations, elementary divisors, invariant factors; quadratic, bi-linear, Hermitian forms, singly and in pairs. Proofs rigorous, detailed; topics developed lucidly, in close connection with their most frequent mathematical applications. Formerly "Modern Algebraic Theories." 155 problems. Bibliography. 2 indexes. 285pp. 5⅜ x 8.　　　　　　S547 Paperbound **$1.50**

LECTURES ON THE ICOSAHEDRON AND THE SOLUTION OF EQUATIONS OF THE FIFTH DEGREE, Felix Klein. The solution of quintics in terms of rotation of a regular icosahedron around its axes of symmetry. A classic & indispensable source for those interested in higher algebra, geometry, crystallography. Considerable explanatory material included. 230 footnotes, mostly bibliographic. 2nd edition, xvi + 289pp. 5⅜ x 8.　　　　　　S314 Paperbound **$2.25**

LINEAR GROUPS, WITH AN EXPOSITION OF THE GALOIS FIELD THEORY, L. E. Dickson. The classic exposition of the theory of groups, well within the range of the graduate student. Part I contains the most extensive and thorough presentation of the theory of Galois Fields available, with a wealth of examples and theorems. Part II is a full discussion of linear groups of finite order. Much material in this work is based on Dickson's own contributions. Also includes expositions of Jordan, Lie, Abel, Betti-Mathieu, Hermite, etc. "A milestone in the development of modern algebra," W. Magnus, in his historical introduction to this edition. Index. xv + 312pp. 5⅜ x 8.　　　　　　S482 Paperbound **$1.95**

INTRODUCTION TO THE THEORY OF GROUPS OF FINITE ORDER, R. Carmichael. Examines fundamental theorems and their application. Beginning with sets, systems, permutations, etc., it progresses in easy stages through important types of groups: Abelian, prime power, permutation, etc. Except 1 chapter where matrices are desirable, no higher math needed. 783 exercises, problems. Index. xvi + 447pp. 5⅜ x 8.　　　　　　S300 Paperbound **$2.25**

THEORY OF GROUPS OF FINITE ORDER, W. Burnside. First published some 40 years ago, this is still one of the clearest introductory texts. Partial contents: permutations, groups independent of representation, composition series of a group, isomorphism of a group with itself, Abelian groups, prime power groups, permutation groups, invariants of groups of linear substitution, graphical representation, etc. 45pp. of notes. Indexes. xxiv + 512pp. 5⅜ x 8.　　　　　　S38 Paperbound **$2.75**

CONTINUOUS GROUPS OF TRANSFORMATIONS, L. P. Eisenhart. Intensive study of the theory and geometrical applications of continuous groups of transformations; a standard work on the subject, called forth by the revolution in physics in the 1920's. Covers tensor analysis, Riemannian geometry, canonical parameters, transitivity, imprimitivity, differential invariants, the algebra of constants of structure, differential geometry, contact transformations, etc. "Likely to remain one of the standard works on the subject for many years . . . principal theorems are proved clearly and concisely, and the arrangement of the whole is coherent," MATHEMATICAL GAZETTE. Index. 72-item bibliography. 185 exercises. ix + 301pp. 5⅜ x 8.　　　　　　S781 Paperbound **$2.00**

THE THEORY OF GROUPS AND QUANTUM MECHANICS, H. Weyl. Discussions of Schroedinger's wave equation, de Broglie's waves of a particle, Jordan-Hoelder theorem, Lie's continuous groups of transformations, Pauli exclusion principle, quantization of Maxwell-Dirac field equations, etc. Unitary geometry, quantum theory, groups, application of groups to quantum mechanics, symmetry permutation group, algebra of symmetric transformation, etc. 2nd revised edition. Bibliography. Index. xxii + 422pp. 5⅜ x 8.　　　　　　S269 Paperbound **$2.35**

APPLIED GROUP-THEORETIC AND MATRIX METHODS, Bryan Higman. The first systematic treatment of group and matrix theory for the physical scientist. Contains a comprehensive, easily-followed exposition of the basic ideas of group theory (realized through matrices) and its applications in the various areas of physics and chemistry: tensor analysis, relativity, quantum theory, molecular structure and spectra, and Eddington's quantum relativity. Includes rigorous proofs available only in works of a far more advanced character. 34 figures, numerous tables. Bibliography. Index. xiii + 454pp. 5⅜ x 8⅜.　　　　　　S1147 Paperbound **$2.50**

THE THEORY OF GROUP REPRESENTATIONS, Francis D. Murnaghan. A comprehensive introduction to the theory of group representations. Particular attention is devoted to those groups—mainly the symmetric and rotation groups—which have proved to be of fundamental significance for quantum mechanics (esp. nuclear physics). Also a valuable contribution to the literature on matrices, since the usual representations of groups are groups of matrices. Covers the theory of group integration (as developed by Schur and Weyl), the theory of 2-valued or spin representations, the representations of the symmetric group, the crystallographic groups, the Lorentz group, reducibility (Schur's lemma, Burnside's Theorem, etc.), the alternating group, linear groups, the orthogonal group, etc. Index. List of references. xi + 369pp. 5⅜ x 8½.　　　　　　S1112 Paperbound **$2.35**

THEORY OF SETS, E. Kamke. Clearest, amplest introduction in English, well suited for independent study. Subdivision of main theory, such as theory of sets of points, are discussed, but emphasis is on general theory. Partial contents: rudiments of set theory, arbitrary sets and their cardinal numbers, ordered sets and their order types, well-ordered sets and their cardinal numbers. Bibliography. Key to symbols. Index. vii + 144pp. 5⅜ x 8.　　　　　　S141 Paperbound **$1.35**

THEORY AND APPLICATIONS OF FINITE GROUPS, G. A. Miller, H. F. Blichfeldt, L. E. Dickson.
Unusually accurate and authoritative work, each section prepared by a leading specialist:
Miller on substitution and abstract groups, Blichfeldt on finite groups of linear homogeneous
transformations, Dickson on applications of finite groups. Unlike more modern works, this gives
the concrete basis from which abstract group theory arose. Includes Abelian groups, prime-
power groups, isomorphisms, matrix forms of linear transformations, Sylow groups, Galois'
theory of algebraic equations, duplication of a cube, trisection of an angle, etc. 2 Indexes.
267 problems. xvii + 390pp. 5⅜ x 8.   S216 Paperbound **$2.00**

THE THEORY OF DETERMINANTS, MATRICES, AND INVARIANTS, H. W. Turnbull. Important
study includes all salient features and major theories. 7 chapters on determinants and
matrices cover fundamental properties, Laplace identities, multiplication, linear equations,
rank and differentiation, etc. Sections on invariants gives general properties, symbolic and
direct methods of reduction, binary and polar forms, general linear transformation, first
fundamental theorem, multilinear forms. Following chapters study development and proof
of Hilbert's Basis Theorem, Gordan-Hilbert Finiteness Theorem, Clebsch's Theorem, and
include discussions of apolarity, canonical forms, geometrical interpretations of algebraic
forms, complete system of the general quadric, etc. New preface and appendix. Bibliography.
xviii + 374pp. 5⅜ x 8.   S699 Paperbound **$2.25**

AN INTRODUCTION TO THE THEORY OF CANONICAL MATRICES, H. W. Turnbull and A. C. Aitken.
All principal aspects of the theory of canonical matrices, from definitions and fundamental
properties of matrices to the practical applications of their reduction to canonical form.
Beginning with matrix multiplications, reciprocals, and partitioned matrices, the authors go
on to elementary transformations and bilinear and quadratic forms. Also covers such topics
as a rational canonical form for the collineatory group, congruent and conjunctive transformation for quadratic and hermitian forms, unitary and orthogonal transformations, canonical
reduction of pencils of matrices, etc. Index. Appendix. Historical notes at chapter ends.
Bibliographies. 275 problems. xiv + 200pp. 5⅜ x 8.   S177 Paperbound **$1.55**

A TREATISE ON THE THEORY OF DETERMINANTS, T. Muir. Unequalled as an exhaustive compila-
tion of nearly all the known facts about determinants up to the early 1930's. Covers notation
and general properties, row and column transformation, symmetry, compound determinants,
adjugates, rectangular arrays and matrices, linear dependence, gradients, Jacobians, Hessians,
Wronskians, and much more. Invaluable for libraries of industrial and research organizations
as well as for student, teacher, and mathematician; very useful in the field of computing
machines. Revised and enlarged by W. H. Metzler. Index. 485 problems and scores of numerical examples. iv + 766pp. 5⅜ x 8.   S670 Paperbound **$3.00**

THEORY OF DETERMINANTS IN THE HISTORICAL ORDER OF DEVELOPMENT, Sir Thomas Muir.
Unabridged reprinting of this complete study of 1,859 papers on determinant theory written
between 1693 and 1900. Most important and original sections reproduced, valuable com-
mentary on each. No other work is necessary for determinant research: all types are covered—
each subdivision of the theory treated separately; all papers dealing with each type are
covered; you are told exactly what each paper is about and how important its contribution is.
Each result, theory, extension, or modification is assigned its own identifying numeral so that
the full history may be more easily followed. Includes papers on determinants in general,
determinants and linear equations, symmetric determinants, alternants, recurrents, determinants having invariant factors, and all other major types. "A model of what such histories
ought to be," NATURE. "Mathematicians must ever be grateful to Sir Thomas for his monumental work," AMERICAN MATH MONTHLY. Four volumes bound as two. Indices. Bibliographies. Total of lxxxiv + 1977pp. 5⅜ x 8.   S672-3 The set, Clothbound **$12.50**

Calculus and function theory, Fourier theory, infinite series, calculus of variations, real and complex functions

FIVE VOLUME "THEORY OF FUNCTIONS' SET BY KONRAD KNOPP

This five-volume set, prepared by Konrad Knopp, provides a complete and readily followed
account of theory of functions. Proofs are given concisely, yet without sacrifice of complete-
ness or rigor. These volumes are used as texts by such universities as M.I.T., University of
Chicago, N. Y. City College, and many others. "Excellent introduction . . . remarkably
readable, concise, clear, rigorous," JOURNAL OF THE AMERICAN STATISTICAL ASSOCIATION.

ELEMENTS OF THE THEORY OF FUNCTIONS, Konrad Knopp. This book provides the student
with background for further volumes in this set, or texts on a similar level. Partial contents:
foundations, system of complex numbers and the Gaussian plane of numbers, Riemann
sphere of numbers, mapping by linear functions, normal forms, the logarithm, the cyclometric
functions and binomial series. "Not only for the young student, but also for the student
who knows all about what is in it," MATHEMATICAL JOURNAL. Bibliography. Index. 140pp.
5⅜ x 8.   S154 Paperbound **$1.35**

THEORY OF FUNCTIONS, PART I, Konrad Knopp. With volume II, this book provides coverage
of basic concepts and theorems. Partial contents: numbers and points, functions of a complex variable, integral of a continuous function, Cauchy's integral theorem, Cauchy's integral
formulae, series with variable terms, expansion of analytic functions in power series, analytic
continuation and complete definition of analytic functions, entire transcendental functions,
Laurent expansion, types of singularities. Bibliography. Index. vii + 146pp. 5⅜ x 8.
                                                                      S156 Paperbound **$1.35**

THEORY OF FUNCTIONS, PART II, Konrad Knopp. Application and further development of general theory, special topics. Single valued functions, entire, Weierstrass, Meromorphic functions. Riemann surfaces. Algebraic functions. Analytical configuration, Riemann surface. Bibliography. Index. x + 150pp. 5⅜ x 8.   S157 Paperbound **$1.35**

PROBLEM BOOK IN THE THEORY OF FUNCTIONS, VOLUME 1, Konrad Knopp. Problems in elementary theory, for use with Knopp's THEORY OF FUNCTIONS, or any other text, arranged according to increasing difficulty. Fundamental concepts, sequences of numbers and infinite series, complex variable, integral theorems, development in series, conformal mapping. 182 problems. Answers. viii + 126pp. 5⅜ x 8.   S158 Paperbound **$1.35**

PROBLEM BOOK IN THE THEORY OF FUNCTIONS, VOLUME 2, Konrad Knopp. Advanced theory of functions, to be used either with Knopp's THEORY OF FUNCTIONS, or any other comparable text. Singularities, entire & meromorphic functions, periodic, analytic, continuation, multiple-valued functions, Riemann surfaces, conformal mapping. Includes a section of additional elementary problems. "The difficult task of selecting from the immense material of the modern theory of functions the problems just within the reach of the beginner is here masterfully accomplished," AM. MATH. SOC. Answers. 138pp. 5⅜ x 8. S159 Paperbound **$1.35**

A COURSE IN MATHEMATICAL ANALYSIS, Edouard Goursat. Trans. by E. R. Hedrick, O. Dunkel. Classic study of fundamental material thoroughly treated. Exceptionally lucid exposition of wide range of subject matter for student with 1 year of calculus. Vol. 1: Derivatives and Differentials, Definite Integrals, Expansion in Series, Applications to Geometry. Problems. Index. 52 illus. 556pp. Vol. 2, Part I: Functions of a Complex Variable, Conformal Representations, Doubly Periodic Functions, Natural Boundaries, etc. Problems. Index. 38 illus. 269pp. Vol. 2, Part 2: Differential Equations, Cauchy-Lipschitz Method, Non-linear Differential Equations, Simultaneous Equations, etc. Problems. Index. 308pp. 5⅜ x 8.

Vol. 1 S554 Paperbound **$2.50**
Vol. 2 part 1 S555 Paperbound **$1.85**
Vol. 2 part 2 S556 Paperbound **$1.85**
3 vol. set **$6.20**

MODERN THEORIES OF INTEGRATION, H. Kestelman. Connected and concrete coverage, with fully-worked-out proofs for every step. Ranges from elementary definitions through theory of aggregates, sets of points, Riemann and Lebesgue integration, and much more. This new revised and enlarged edition contains a new chapter on Riemann-Stieltjes integration, as well as a supplementary section of 186 exercises. Ideal for the mathematician, student, teacher, or self-studier. Index of Definitions and Symbols. General Index. Bibliography. x + 310pp. 5⅝ x 8⅜.   S572 Paperbound **$2.25**

THEORY OF MAXIMA AND MINIMA, H. Hancock. Fullest treatment ever written; only work in English with extended discussion of maxima and minima for functions of 1, 2, or n variables, problems with subsidiary constraints, and relevant quadratic forms. Detailed proof of each important theorem. Covers the Scheeffer and von Dantscher theories, homogeneous quadratic forms, reversion of series, fallacious establishment of maxima and minima, etc. Unsurpassed treatise for advanced students of calculus, mathematicians, economists, statisticians. Index. 24 diagrams. 39 problems, many examples. 193pp. 5⅜ x 8.   S665 Paperbound **$1.50**

AN ELEMENTARY TREATISE ON ELLIPTIC FUNCTIONS, A. Cayley. Still the fullest and clearest text on the theories of Jacobi and Legendre for the advanced student (and an excellent supplement for the beginner). A masterpiece of exposition by the great 19th century British mathematician (creator of the theory of matrices and abstract geometry), it covers the addition-theory, Landen's theorem, the 3 kinds of elliptic integrals, transformations, the q-functions, reduction of a differential expression, and much more. Index. xii + 386pp. 5⅜ x 8.
S728 Paperbound **$2.00**

THE APPLICATIONS OF ELLIPTIC FUNCTIONS, A. G. Greenhill. Modern books forego detail for sake of brevity—this book offers complete exposition necessary for proper understanding, use of elliptic integrals. Formulas developed from definite physical, geometric problems; examples representative enough to offer basic information in widely useable form. Elliptic integrals, addition theorem, algebraical form of addition theorem, elliptic integrals of 2nd, 3rd kind, double periodicity, resolution into factors, series, transformation, etc. Introduction. Index. 25 illus. xi + 357pp. 5⅜ x 8.   S603 Paperbound **$1.75**

THE THEORY OF FUNCTIONS OF REAL VARIABLES, James Pierpont. A 2-volume authoritative exposition, by one of the foremost mathematicians of his time. Each theorem stated with all conditions, then followed by proof. No need to go through complicated reasoning to discover conditions added without specific mention. Includes a particularly complete, rigorous presentation of theory of measure; and Pierpont's own work on a theory of Lebesgue integrals, and treatment of area of a curved surface. Partial contents, Vol. 1: rational numbers, exponentials, logarithms, point aggregates, maxima, minima, proper integrals, improper integrals, multiple proper integrals, continuity, discontinuity, indeterminate forms. Vol. 2: point sets, proper integrals, series, power series, aggregates, ordinal numbers, discontinuous functions, sub-, infra-uniform convergence, much more. Index. 95 illustrations. 1229pp. 5⅜ x 8.   S558-9, 2 volume set, paperbound **$5.20**

FUNCTIONS OF A COMPLEX VARIABLE, James Pierpont. Long one of best in the field. A thorough treatment of fundamental elements, concepts, theorems. A complete study, rigorous, detailed, with carefully selected problems worked out to illustrate each topic. Partial contents: arithmetical operations, real term series, positive term series, exponential functions, integration, analytic functions, asymptotic expansions, functions of Weierstrass, Legendre, etc. Index. List of symbols. 122 illus. 597pp. 5⅜ x 8. S560 Paperbound **$2.45**

MODERN OPERATIONAL CALCULUS: WITH APPLICATIONS IN TECHNICAL MATHEMATICS, N. W. McLachlan. An introduction to modern operational calculus based upon the Laplace transform, applying it to the solution of ordinary and partial differential equations. For physicists, engineers, and applied mathematicians. Partial contents: Laplace transform, theorems or rules of the operational calculus, solution of ordinary and partial linear differential equations with constant coefficients, evaluation of integrals and establishment of mathematical relationships, derivation of Laplace transforms of various functions, etc. Six appendices deal with Heaviside's unit function, etc. Revised edition. Index. Bibliography. xiv + 218pp. 5⅜ x 8½. S192 Paperbound **$1.75**

ADVANCED CALCULUS, E. B. Wilson. An unabridged reprinting of the work which continues to be recognized as one of the most comprehensive and useful texts in the field. It contains an immense amount of well-presented, fundamental material, including chapters on vector functions, ordinary differential equations, special functions, calculus of variations, etc., which are excellent introductions to these areas. For students with only one year of calculus, more than 1300 exercises cover both pure math and applications to engineering and physical problems. For engineers, physicists, etc., this work, with its 54 page introductory review, is the ideal reference and refresher. Index. ix + 566pp. 5⅜ x 8. S504 Paperbound **$2.45**

ASYMPTOTIC EXPANSIONS, A. Erdélyi. The only modern work available in English, this is an unabridged reproduction of a monograph prepared for the Office of Naval Research. It discusses various procedures for asymptotic evaluation of integrals containing a large parameter and solutions of ordinary linear differential equations. Bibliography of 71 items. vi + 108pp. 5⅜ x 8. S318 Paperbound **$1.35**

INTRODUCTION TO ELLIPTIC FUNCTIONS: with applications, F. Bowman. Concise, practical introduction to elliptic integrals and functions. Beginning with the familiar trigonometric functions, it requires nothing more from the reader than a knowledge of basic principles of differentiation and integration. Discussion confined to the Jacobian functions. Enlarged bibliography. Index. 173 problems and examples. 56 figures, 4 tables. 115pp. 5⅜ x 8. S922 Paperbound **$1.25**

ON RIEMANN'S THEORY OF ALGEBRAIC FUNCTIONS AND THEIR INTEGRALS: A SUPPLEMENT TO THE USUAL TREATISES, Felix Klein. Klein demonstrates how the mathematical ideas in Riemann's work on Abelian integrals can be arrived at by thinking in terms of the flow of electric current on surfaces. Intuitive explanations, not detailed proofs given in an extremely clear exposition, concentrating on the kinds of functions which can be defined on Riemann surfaces. Also useful as an introduction to the origins of topological problems. Complete and unabridged. Approved translation by Frances Hardcastle. New introduction. 43 figures. Glossary. xii + 76pp. 5⅜ x 8½. S1072 Paperbound **$1.25**

COLLECTED WORKS OF BERNHARD RIEMANN. This important source book is the first to contain the complete text of both 1892 Werke and the 1902 supplement, unabridged. It contains 31 monographs, 3 complete lecture courses, 15 miscellaneous papers, which have been of enormous importance in relativity, topology, theory of complex variables, and other areas of mathematics. Edited by R. Dedekind, H. Weber, M. Noether, W. Wirtinger. German text. English introduction by Hans Lewy. 690pp. 5⅜ x 8. S226 Paperbound **$3.75**

THE TAYLOR SERIES, AN INTRODUCTION TO THE THEORY OF FUNCTIONS OF A COMPLEX VARIABLE, P. Dienes. This book investigates the entire realm of analytic functions. Only ordinary calculus is needed, except in the last two chapters. Starting with an introduction to real variables and complex algebra, the properties of infinite series, elementary functions, complex differentiation and integration are carefully derived. Also biuniform mapping, a thorough two part discussion of representation and singularities of analytic functions, overconvergence and gap theorems, divergent series, Taylor series on its circle of convergence, divergence and singularities, etc. Unabridged, corrected reissue of first edition. Preface and index. 186 examples, many fully worked out. 67 figures. xii + 555pp. 5⅜ x 8. S391 Paperbound **$2.75**

INTRODUCTION TO BESSEL FUNCTIONS, Frank Bowman. A rigorous self-contained exposition providing all necessary material during the development, which requires only some knowledge of calculus and acquaintance with differential equations. A balanced presentation including applications and practical use. Discusses Bessel Functions of Zero Order, of Any Real Order; Modified Bessel Functions of Zero Order; Definite Integrals; Asymptotic Expansions; Bessel's Solution to Kepler's Problem; Circular Membranes; much more. "Clear and straightforward . . . useful not only to students of physics and engineering, but to mathematical students in general," Nature. 226 problems. Short tables of Bessel functions. 27 figures. Index. x + 135pp. 5⅜ x 8. S462 Paperbound **$1.35**

Catalogue of Dover Books

ELEMENTS OF THE THEORY OF REAL FUNCTIONS, J. E. Littlewood. Based on lectures given at Trinity College, Cambridge, this book has proved to be extremely successful in introducing graduate students to the modern theory of functions. It offers a full and concise coverage of classes and cardinal numbers, well-ordered series, other types of series, and elements of the theory of sets of points. 3rd revised edition. vii + 71pp. 5⅜ x 8.
S171 Clothbound **$2.85**
S172 Paperbound **$1.25**

TRANSCENDENTAL AND ALGEBRAIC NUMBERS, A. O. Gelfond. First English translation of work by leading Soviet mathematician. Thue-Siegel theorem, its p-adic analogue, on approximation of algebraic numbers by numbers in fixed algebraic field; Hermite-Lindemann theorem on transcendency of Bessel functions, solutions of other differential equations; Gelfond-Schneider theorem on transcendency of alpha to power beta; Schneider's work on elliptic functions, with method developed by Gelfond. Translated by L. F. Boron. Index. Bibliography. 200pp. 5⅜ x 8.
S615 Paperbound **$1.75**

ELLIPTIC INTEGRALS, H. Hancock. Invaluable in work involving differential equations containing cubics or quartics under the root sign, where elementary calculus methods are inadequate. Practical solutions to problems that occur in mathematics, engineering, physics: differential equations requiring integration of Lamé's, Briot's, or Bouquet's equations; determination of arc of ellipse, hyperbola, lemniscate; solutions of problems in elastica; motion of a projectile under resistance varying as the cube of the velocity; pendulums; many others. Exposition is in accordance with Legendre-Jacobi theory and includes rigorous discussion of Legendre transformations. 20 figures. 5 place table. Index. 104pp. 5⅛ x 8.
S484 Paperbound **$1.25**

LECTURES ON THE THEORY OF ELLIPTIC FUNCTIONS, H. Hancock. Reissue of the only book in English with so extensive a coverage, especially of Abel, Jacobi, Legendre, Weierstrasse, Hermite, Liouville, and Riemann. Unusual fullness of treatment, plus applications as well as theory, in discussing elliptic function (the universe of elliptic integrals originating in works of Abel and Jacobi), their existence, and ultimate meaning. Use is made of Riemann to provide the most general theory. 40 page table of formulas. 76 figures. xxiii + 498pp.
S483 Paperbound **$2.55**

THE THEORY AND FUNCTIONS OF A REAL VARIABLE AND THE THEORY OF FOURIER'S SERIES, E. W. Hobson. One of the best introductions to set theory and various aspects of functions and Fourier's series. Requires only a good background in calculus. Provides an exhaustive coverage of: metric and descriptive properties of sets of points; transfinite numbers and order types; functions of a real variable; the Riemann and Lebesgue integrals; sequences and series of numbers; power-series; functions representable by series sequences of continuous functions; trigonometrical series; representation of functions by Fourier's series; complete exposition (200pp.) on set theory; and much more. "The best possible guide," Nature. Vol. I: 88 detailed examples, 10 figures. Index. xv + 736pp. Vol. II: 117 detailed examples, 13 figures. Index. x + 780pp. 6⅛ x 9¼.
Vol. I: S387 Paperbound **$3.00**
Vol. II: S388 Paperbound **$3.00**

ALMOST PERIODIC FUNCTIONS, A. S. Besicovitch. This unique and important summary by a well-known mathematician covers in detail the two stages of development in Bohr's theory of almost periodic functions: (1) as a generalization of pure periodicity, with results and proofs; (2) the work done by Stepanoff, Wiener, Weyl, and Bohr in generalizing the theory. Bibliography. xi + 180pp. 5⅜ x 8.
S18 Paperbound **$1.75**

THE ANALYTICAL THEORY OF HEAT, Joseph Fourier. This book, which revolutionized mathematical physics, is listed in the Great Books program, and many other listings of great books. It has been used with profit by generations of mathematicians and physicists who are interested in either heat or in the application of the Fourier integral. Covers cause and reflection of rays of heat, radiant heating, heating of closed spaces, use of trigonometric series in the theory of heat, Fourier integral, etc. Translated by Alexander Freeman. 20 figures. xxii + 466pp. 5⅜ x 8.
S93 Paperbound **$2.50**

AN INTRODUCTION TO FOURIER METHODS AND THE LAPLACE TRANSFORMATION, Philip Franklin. Concentrates upon essentials, enabling the reader with only a working knowledge of calculus to gain an understanding of Fourier methods in a broad sense, suitable for most applications. This work covers complex qualities with methods of computing elementary functions for complex values of the argument and finding approximations by the use of charts; Fourier series and integrals with half-range and complex Fourier series; harmonic analysis; Fourier and Laplace transformations, etc.; partial differential equations with applications to transmission of electricity; etc. The methods developed are related to physical problems of heat flow, vibrations, electrical transmission, electromagnetic radiation, etc. 828 problems with answers. Formerly entitled "Fourier Methods." Bibliography. Index. x + 289pp. 5⅜ x 8.
S452 Paperbound **$2.00**

THE FOURIER INTEGRAL AND CERTAIN OF ITS APPLICATIONS, Norbert Wiener. The only book-length study of the Fourier integral as link between pure and applied math. An expansion of lectures given at Cambridge. Partial contents: Plancherel's theorem, general Tauberian theorem, special Tauberian theorems, generalized harmonic analysis. Bibliography. viii + 201pp. 5⅜ x 8.
S272 Paperbound **$1.50**

Differential equations, ordinary and partial; integral equations

INTRODUCTION TO THE DIFFERENTIAL EQUATIONS OF PHYSICS, L. Hopf. Especially valuable to the engineer with no math beyond elementary calculus. Emphasizing intuitive rather than formal aspects of concepts, the author covers an extensive territory. Partial contents: Law of causality, energy theorem, damped oscillations, coupling by friction, cylindrical and spherical coordinates, heat source, etc. Index. 48 figures. 160pp. 5⅜ x 8.
S120 Paperbound **$1.25**

INTRODUCTION TO THE THEORY OF LINEAR DIFFERENTIAL EQUATIONS, E. G. Poole. Authoritative discussions of important topics, with methods of solution more detailed than usual, for students with background of elementary course in differential equations. Studies existence theorems, linearly independent solutions; equations with constant coefficients; with uniform analytic coefficients; regular singularities; the hypergeometric equation; conformal representation; etc. Exercises. Index. 210pp. 5⅜ x 8.
S629 Paperbound **$1.65**

DIFFERENTIAL EQUATIONS FOR ENGINEERS, P. Franklin. Outgrowth of a course given 10 years at M. I. T. Makes most useful branch of pure math accessible for practical work. Theoretical basis of D.E.'s; solution of ordinary D.E.'s and partial derivatives arising from heat flow, steady-state temperature of a plate, wave equations; analytic functions; convergence of Fourier Series. 400 problems on electricity, vibratory systems, other topics. Formerly "Differential Equations for Electrical Engineers." Index 41 illus. 307pp. 5⅜ x 8.
S601 Paperbound **$1.65**

DIFFERENTIAL EQUATIONS, F. R. Moulton. A detailed, rigorous exposition of all the non-elementary processes of solving ordinary differential equations. Several chapters devoted to the treatment of practical problems, especially those of a physical nature, which are far more advanced than problems usually given as illustrations. Includes analytic differential equations; variations of a parameter; integrals of differential equations; analytic implicit functions; problems of elliptic motion; sine-amplitude functions; deviation of formal bodies; Cauchy-Lipschitz process; linear differential equations with periodic coefficients; differential equations in infinitely many variations; much more. Historical notes. 10 figures. 222 problems. Index. xv + 395pp. 5⅜ x 8.
S451 Paperbound **$2.00**

DIFFERENTIAL AND INTEGRAL EQUATIONS OF MECHANICS AND PHYSICS (DIE DIFFERENTIAL-UND INTEGRALGLEICHUNGEN DER MECHANIK UND PHYSIK), edited by P. Frank and R. von Mises. Most comprehensive and authoritative work on the mathematics of mathematical physics available today in the United States: the standard, definitive reference for teachers, physicists, engineers, and mathematicians—now published (in the original German) at a relatively inexpensive price for the first time! Every chapter in this 2,000-page set is by an expert in his field: Carathéodory, Courant, Frank, Mises, and a dozen others. Vol I, on mathematics, gives concise but complete coverages of advanced calculus, differential equations, integral equations, and potential, and partial differential equations. Index. xxiii + 916pp. Vol. II (physics): classical mechanics, optics, continuous mechanics, heat conduction and diffusion, the stationary and quasi-stationary electromagnetic field, electromagnetic oscillations, and wave mechanics. Index. xxiv + 1106pp. Two volume set. Each volume available separately. 5⅝ x 8⅜.
S787 Vol I Clothbound **$7.50**
S788 Vol II Clothbound **$7.50**
The set **$15.00**

LECTURES ON CAUCHY'S PROBLEM, J. Hadamard. Based on lectures given at Columbia, Rome, this discusses work of Riemann, Kirchhoff, Volterra, and the author's own research on the hyperbolic case in linear partial differential equations. It extends spherical and cylindrical waves to apply to all (normal) hyperbolic equations. Partial contents: Cauchy's problem, fundamental formula, equations with odd number, with even number of independent variables; method of descent. 32 figures. Index. iii + 316pp. 5⅜ x 8.   S105 Paperbound **$1.75**

THEORY OF DIFFERENTIAL EQUATIONS, A. R. Forsyth. Out of print for over a decade, the complete 6 volumes (now bound as 3) of this monumental work represent the most comprehensive treatment of differential equations ever written. Historical presentation includes in 2500 pages every substantial development. Vol. 1, 2: EXACT EQUATIONS, PFAFF'S PROBLEM; ORDINARY EQUATIONS, NOT LINEAR: methods of Grassmann, Clebsch, Lie, Darboux; Cauchy's theorem; branch points; etc. Vol. 3, 4: ORDINARY EQUATIONS, NOT LINEAR; ORDINARY LINEAR EQUATIONS: Zeta Fuchsian functions, general theorems on algebraic integrals, Brun's theorem, equations with uniform periodic coefficients, etc. Vol. 4, 5: PARTIAL DIFFERENTIAL EQUATIONS: 2 existence-theorems, equations of theoretical dynamics, Laplace transformations, general transformation of equations of the 2nd order, much more. Indexes. Total of 2766pp. 5⅜ x 8.   S576-7-8 Clothbound: the set **$15.00**

PARTIAL DIFFERENTIAL EQUATIONS OF MATHEMATICAL PHYSICS, A. G. Webster. A keystone work in the library of every mature physicist, engineer, researcher. Valuable sections on elasticity, compression theory, potential theory, theory of sound, heat conduction, wave propagation, vibration theory. Contents include: deduction of differential equations, vibrations, normal functions, Fourier's series, Cauchy's method, boundary problems, method of Riemann-Volterra. Spherical, cylindrical, ellipsoidal harmonics, applications, etc. 97 figures. vii + 440pp. 5⅜ x 8.   S263 Paperbound **$2.00**

Probability theory and information theory

AN ELEMENTARY INTRODUCTION TO THE THEORY OF PROBABILITY, B. V. Gnedenko and A. Ya. Khinchin. Translated by Leo F. Boron. A clear, compact introduction designed to equip the reader with a fundamental grasp of the theory of probability. It is thorough and authoritative within its purposely restricted range, yet the layman with a background in elementary mathematics will be able to follow it without difficulty. Covers such topics as the processes involved in the calculation of probabilities, conditional probabilities and the multiplication rule, Bayes's formula, Bernoulli's scheme and theorem, random variables and distribution laws, and dispersion and mean deviations. New translation of fifth (revised) Russian edition (1960)—the only translation checked and corrected by Gnedenko. New preface for Dover edition by B. V. Gnedenko. Index. Bibliography. Appendix: Table of values of function $\phi(a)$. xii + 130pp. 5⅜ x 8½.   T155 Paperbound **$1.50**

AN INTRODUCTION TO MATHEMATICAL PROBABILITY, Julian Lowell Coolidge. A thorough introduction which presents the mathematical foundation of the theory of probability. A substantial body of material, yet can be understood with a knowledge of only elementary calculus. Contains: The Scope and Meaning of Mathematical Probability; Elementary Principles of Probability; Bernoulli's Theorem; Mean Value and Dispersion; Geometrical Probability; Probability of Causes; Errors of Observation; Errors in Many Variables; Indirect Observations; The Statistical Theory of Gases; and The Principles of Life Insurance. Six pages of logarithm tables. 4 diagrams. Subject and author indices. xii + 214pp. 5⅜ x 8½.
S258 Paperbound **$1.35**

A GUIDE TO OPERATIONS RESEARCH, W. E. Duckworth. A brief nontechnical exposition of techniques and theories of operational research. A good introduction for the layman; also can provide the initiate with new understandings. No mathematical training needed, yet not an oversimplification. Covers game theory, mathematical analysis, information theory, linear programming, cybernetics, decision theory, etc. Also includes a discussion of the actual organization of an operational research program and an account of the uses of such programs in the oil, chemical, paper, and metallurgical industries, etc. Bibliographies at chapter ends. Appendices. 36 figures. 145pp. 5¼ x 8½.   T1129 Clothbound **$3.50**

MATHEMATICAL FOUNDATIONS OF INFORMATION THEORY, A. I. Khinchin. For the first time mathematicians, statisticians, physicists, cyberneticists, and communications engineers are offered a complete and exact introduction to this relatively new field. Entropy as a measure of a finite scheme, applications to coding theory, study of sources, channels and codes, detailed proofs of both Shannon theorems for any ergodic source and any stationary channel with finite memory, and much more are covered. Bibliography. vii + 120pp. 5⅜ x 8.
S434 Paperbound **$1.35**

SELECTED PAPERS ON NOISE AND STOCHASTIC PROCESS, edited by Prof. Nelson Wax, U. of Illinois. 6 basic papers for newcomers in the field, for those whose work involves noise characteristics. Chandrasekhar, Uhlenbeck & Ornstein, Uhlenbeck & Ming, Rice, Doob. Included is Kac's Chauvenet-Prize winning Random Walk. Extensive bibliography lists 200 articles, up through 1953. 21 figures. 337pp. 6⅛ x 9¼.   S262 Paperbound **$2.50**

THEORY OF PROBABILITY, William Burnside. Synthesis, expansion of individual papers presents numerous problems in classical probability, offering many original views succinctly, effectively. Game theory, cards, selections from groups; geometrical probability in such areas as suppositions as to probability of position of point on a line, points on surface of sphere, etc. Includes methods of approximation, theory of errors, direct calculation of probabilities, etc. Index. 136pp. 5⅜ x 8.   S567 Paperbound **$1.00**

Statistics

ELEMENTARY STATISTICS, WITH APPLICATIONS IN MEDICINE AND THE BIOLOGICAL SCIENCES, F. E. Croxton. A sound introduction to statistics for anyone in the physical sciences, assuming no prior acquaintance and requiring only a modest knowledge of math. All basic formulas carefully explained and illustrated; all necessary reference tables included. From basic terms and concepts, the study proceeds to frequency distribution, linear, non-linear, and multiple correlation, skewness, kurtosis, etc. A large section deals with reliability and significance of statistical methods. Containing concrete examples from medicine and biology, this book will prove unusually helpful to workers in those fields who increasingly must evaluate, check, and interpret statistics. Formerly titled "Elementary Statistics with Applications in Medicine." 101 charts. 57 tables. 14 appendices. Index. iv + 376pp. 5⅜ x 8.
S506 Paperbound **$2.00**

ANALYSIS & DESIGN OF EXPERIMENTS, H. B. Mann. Offers a method for grasping the analysis of variance and variance design within a short time. Partial contents: Chi-square distribution and analysis of variance distribution, matrices, quadratic forms, likelihood ration tests and tests of linear hypotheses, power of analysis, Galois fields, non-orthogonal data, interblock estimates, etc. 15pp. of useful tables. x + 195pp. 5 x 7⅜.   S180 Paperbound **$1.45**

Catalogue of Dover Books

METHODS OF STATISTICS, L. H. C. Tippett. A classic in its field, this unusually complete systematic introduction to statistical methods begins at beginner's level and progresses to advanced levels for experimenters and poll-takers in all fields of statistical research. Supplies fundamental knowledge of virtually all elementary methods in use today by sociologists, psychologists, biologists, engineers, mathematicians, etc. Explains logical and mathematical basis of each method described, with examples for each section. Covers frequency distributions and measures, inference from random samples, errors in large samples, simple analysis of variance, multiple and partial regression and correlation, etc. 4th revised (1952) edition. 16 charts. 5 significance tables. 152-item bibliography. 96 tables. 22 figures. 395pp. 6 x 9.
S228 Clothbound **$7.50**

STATISTICS MANUAL, E. L. Crow, F. A. Davis, M. W. Maxfield. Comprehensive collection of classical, modern statistics methods, prepared under auspices of U. S. Naval Ordnance Test Station, China Lake, Calif. Many examples from ordnance will be valuable to workers in all fields. Emphasis is on use, with information on fiducial limits, sign tests, Chi-square runs, sensitivity, quality control, much more. "Well written . . . excellent reference work," Operations Research. Corrected edition of NAVORD Report 3360 NOTS 948. Introduction. Appendix of 32 tables, charts. Index. Bibliography. 95 illustrations. 306pp. 5⅜ x 8.
S599 Paperbound **$1.75**

Symbolic logic

AN INTRODUCTION TO SYMBOLIC LOGIC, Susanne K. Langer. Probably the clearest book ever written on symbolic logic for the philosopher, general scientist and layman. It will be particularly appreciated by those who have been rebuffed by other introductory works because of insufficient mathematical training. No special knowledge of mathematics is required. Starting with the simplest symbols and conventions, you are led to a remarkable grasp of the Boole-Schroeder and Russell-Whitehead systems clearly and quickly. PARTIAL CONTENTS: Study of forms, Essentials of logical structure, Generalization, Classes, The deductive system of classes, The algebra of logic, Abstraction of interpretation, Calculus of propositions, Assumptions of PRINCIPIA MATHEMATICA, Logistics, Logic of the syllogism, Proofs of theorems. "One of the clearest and simplest introductions to a subject which is very much alive. The style is easy, symbolism is introduced gradually, and the intelligent non-mathematician should have no difficulty in following the argument," MATHEMATICS GAZETTE. Revised, expanded second edition. Truth-value tables. 368pp. 5⅜ x 8.
S164 Paperbound **$1.75**

A SURVEY OF SYMBOLIC LOGIC: THE CLASSIC ALGEBRA OF LOGIC, C. I. Lewis. Classic survey of the field, comprehensive and thorough. Indicates content of major systems, alternative methods of procedure, and relation of these to the Boole-Schroeder algebra and to one another. Contains historical summary, as well as full proofs and applications of the classic, or Boole-Schroeder, algebra of logic. Discusses diagrams for the logical relations of classes, the two-valued algebra, propositional functions of two or more variables, etc. Chapters 5 and 6 of the original edition, which contained material not directly pertinent, have been omitted in this edition at the author's request. Appendix. Bibliography. Index. viii + 352pp. 5⅝ x 8⅜.
S643 Paperbound **$2.00**

INTRODUCTION TO SYMBOLIC LOGIC AND ITS APPLICATIONS, R. Carnap. One of the clearest, most comprehensive, and rigorous introductions to modern symbolic logic by perhaps its greatest living master. Symbolic languages are analyzed and one constructed. Applications to math (symbolic representation of axiom systems for set theory, natural numbers, real numbers, topology, Dedekind and Cantor explanations of continuity), physics (the general analysis of concepts of determination, causality, space-time-topology, based on Einstein), biology (symbolic representation of an axiom system for basic concepts). "A masterpiece," Zentralblatt für Mathematik und ihre Grenzgebiete. Over 300 exercises. 5 figures. Bibliography. Index. xvi + 241pp. 5⅜ x 8.
S453 Paperbound **$1.85**
Clothbound **$4.00**

SYMBOLIC LOGIC, C. I. Lewis, C. H. Langford. Probably the most cited book in symbolic logic, this is one of the fullest treatments of paradoxes. A wide coverage of the entire field of symbolic logic, plus considerable material that has not appeared elsewhere. Basic to the entire volume is the distinction between the logic of extensions and of intensions. Considerable emphasis is placed on converse substitution, while the matrix system presents the supposition of a variety of non-Aristotelian logics. It has especially valuable sections on strict limitations, existence of terms, 2-valued algebra and its extension to propositional functions, truth value systems, the matrix method, implication and deductibility, general theory of propositions, propositions of ordinary discourse, and similar topics. "Authoritative, most valuable," TIMES, London. Bibliography. 506pp. 5⅜ x 8.
S170 Paperbound **$2.35**

THE ELEMENTS OF MATHEMATICAL LOGIC, Paul Rosenbloom. First publication in any language. This book is intended for readers who are mature mathematically, but have no previous training in symbolic logic. It does not limit itself to a single system, but covers the field as a whole. It is a development of lectures given at Lund University, Sweden, in 1948. Partial contents: Logic of classes, fundamental theorems, Boolean algebra, logic of propositions, logic of propositional functions, expressive languages, combinatory logics, development of mathematics within an object language, paradoxes, theorems of Post and Goedel, Church's theorem, and similar topics. iv + 214pp. 5⅜ x 8. S227 Paperbound **$1.45**

Catalogue of Dover Books

THE PRINCIPLES OF SCIENCE, A TREATISE ON LOGIC AND THE SCIENTIFIC METHOD, W. S. Jevons. Treating such topics as Inductive and Deductive Logic, the Theory of Number, Probability, and the Limits of Scientific Method, this milestone in the development of symbolic logic remains a stimulating contribution to the investigation of inferential validity in the natural and social sciences. It significantly advances Boole's logic, and contains a detailed introduction to the nature and methods of probability in physics, astronomy, everyday affairs, etc. In his introduction, Ernest Nagel of Columbia University says, "[Jevons] continues to be of interest as an attempt to articulate the logic of scientific inquiry." Index. liii + 786pp. 5⅜ x 8. S446 Paperbound **$2.98**

Vector and tensor analysis

VECTOR AND TENSOR ANALYSIS, A. P. Wills. Covers the entire field of vector and tensor analysis from elementary notions to dyads and non-Euclidean manifolds (especially detailed), absolute differentiation, the Lamé operator, the Riemann-Christoffel and Ricci-Einstein tensors, and the calculation of the Gaussian curvature of a surface. Many illustrations from electrical engineering, relativity theory, astro-physics, quantum mechanics. Presupposes only a good working knowledge of calculus. Exercises at end of each chapter. Intended for physicists and engineers as well as pure mathematicians. 44 diagrams. 114 problems. Bibliography. Index. xxxii + 285pp. 5⅜ x 8. S454 Paperbound **$1.75**

APPLICATIONS OF TENSOR ANALYSIS, A. J. McConnell. (Formerly APPLICATIONS OF THE ABSOLUTE DIFFERENTIAL CALCULUS.) An excellent text for understanding the application of tensor methods to familiar subjects such as dynamics, electricity, elasticity, and hydrodynamics. Explains the fundamental ideas and notation of tensor theory, the geometrical treatment of tensor algebra, the theory of differentiation of tensors, and includes a wealth of practical material. Bibliography. Index. 43 illustrations. 685 problems. xii + 381pp. 5⅜ x 8. S373 Paperbound **$1.95**

VECTOR AND TENSOR ANALYSIS, G. E. Hay. One of the clearest introductions to this increasingly important subject. Start with simple definitions, finish the book with a sure mastery of oriented Cartesian vectors, Christoffel symbols, solenoidal tensors, and their applications. Complete breakdown of plane, solid, analytical, differential geometry. Separate chapters on application. All fundamental formulae listed & demonstrated. 195 problems, 66 figures. viii + 193pp. 5⅜ x 8. S109 Paperbound **$1.85**

VECTOR ANALYSIS, FOUNDED UPON THE LECTURES OF J. WILLARD GIBBS, by E. B. Wilson. Still a first-rate introduction and supplementary text for students of mathematics and physics. Based on the pioneering lectures of Yale's great J. Willard Gibbs, can be followed by anyone who has had some calculus. Practical approach, stressing efficient use of combinations and functions of vectors. Worked examples from geometry, mechanics, hydrodynamics, gas theory, etc., as well as practice examples. Covers basic vector processes, differential and integral calculus in relation to vector functions, and theory of linear vector functions, forming an introduction to the study of multiple algebra and matrix theory. While the notation is not always modern, it is easily followed. xviii + 436pp. 5⅜ x 8. S656 Paperbound **$2.25**

PROBLEMS AND WORKED SOLUTIONS IN VECTOR ANALYSIS, L. R. Shorter. More pages of fully-worked-out examples than any other text on vector analysis. A self-contained course for home study or a fine classroom supplement. 138 problems and examples begin with fundamentals, then cover systems of coordinates, relative velocity and acceleration, the commutative and distributive laws, axial and polar vectors, finite displacements, the calculus of vectors, curl and divergence, etc. Final chapter treats applications in dynamics and physics: kinematics of a rigid body, equipotential surfaces, etc. "Very helpful . . . very comprehensive. A handy book like this . . . will fill a great want," MATHEMATICAL GAZETTE. Index. List of 174 important equations. 158 figures. xiv + 356pp. 5⅜ x 8. S135 Paperbound **$2.00**

Prices subject to change without notice.

Dover publishes books on art, music, philosophy, literature, languages, history, social sciences, psychology, handcrafts, orientalia, puzzles and entertainments, chess, pets and gardens, books explaining science, intermediate and higher mathematics, mathematical physics, engineering, biological sciences, earth sciences, classics of science, etc. Write to:

Dept. catrr.
Dover Publications, Inc.
180 Varick Street, N.Y. 14, N.Y.